MORE YEARS
ON THE TRACTOR SEAT

MORE YEARS
ON THE TRACTOR SEAT

Arthur Battelle

FARMING PRESS

ISBN 0 85236 315 X

A catalogue record for this book is available
from the British Library

Published by Farming Press Books
Miller Freeman Professional Ltd
Wharfedale Road, Ipswich IP1 4LG, United Kingdom

Distributed in North America
by Diamond Farm Enterprises,
Box 537, Alexandria Bay, NY 13607, USA

The photograph on the front cover shows the author
ploughing in the 1960s

The illustration on the back cover shows an
I.H. B450 tractor and a B45 baler

Cover design by Mark Beesley

Typeset by Galleon Typesetting
Printed and bound in Great Britain by Biddles Ltd,
Guildford and King's Lynn

PREFACE

THOSE of you who have read my first book, *Early Years on the Tractor Seat* will, I hope, readily accommodate yourselves with this second and continuing story; but those who have not ventured into my first set of ramblings about using tractors during and just after the Second World War may need some explanation of how the title *More Years on the Tractor Seat* can be reconciled with the opening of this book, that speaks mostly about cows and milking machines. But fear not – all will be revealed in due course.

My experiences as a farmer, cultivation contractor, agricultural engineer, tractor demonstrator for a dealer and later a manufacturer are all in here somewhere, as are my memories of some of the wonderful people who have helped me along the way. I hope no confidences have been abused. It is not my intention to embarrass anyone other than myself and if this is to be an accurate account of my life with tractors some embarrassment to me is inevitable.

ARTHUR BATTELLE

1

FOR me 1949 was a year of freedom. It may be that those of you who can remember that far back do not agree – after all those were the days of strict rationing, even so long after the finish of the Second World War. But to me, with a new job and a new wife to share life with, it really meant freedom: no parents to give advice, however well meant, no travelling to the seaside with Betty and selecting a guest house where we needed to adopt the 'Mr and Mrs' guise or pay for two rooms one of which we never intended to use. Freedom indeed.

The Crossley car and our 14 foot caravan was a fine first home but as we began to collect more household goods the caravan became more and more overloaded. The Crossley's Coventry Climax engine began to find pulling us around a job it could not cope with. This finally came to a head on a journey to fit a milking machine near Melton Mowbray. Halfway up a steep rise we came to a stop. Betty pushed; the car clutch was slipped mercilessly, to try and lift off again. But all in vain – we were stuck. Looking around for salvation we spied a farm across a field. The farmer was most helpful, pulling us to the top of the hill with his grey Fergie tractor. However we never had total confidence in the Crossley again.

Our destination was a farm in the village of Wymond-ham. The farmer's Christian name was Elijah, an unusual name, so it sticks in my mind, but for the life of me his surname escapes me; neither can I remember if the farm was run by two brothers and a sister or two sisters and a brother. But Elijah was the central figure – a very pleasant and helpful man who ran an efficient and clean farm.

Maybe in our newly married state we were spending too much time together, with two-hour lunch breaks and prolonged afternoon teas; anyway Elijah had to point out that he felt I was not getting on quick enough with the installation so perhaps more effort should be put into the milking machine whilst attention to the wellbeing of my wife perhaps could be concentrated into the evening – after all he was paying £1 10s per week lodging allowance to keep me on the farm.

He was of course quite correct, so our newly married bliss had to be reorganised. At the end of our second week with him the installation was complete and we were ready to start the exciting time of introducing the new machine to his bovine ladies.

Unknown to me we had hit a critical time on the farm. One of the family was to be absent for three days and this did not fit well with the start-up of the machine because it was felt that all members of the family should be present for the instruction period and of course to help with the extra demands the start-up would inevitably make with the new procedures to be learned. So now we had four days to kill. It would be nice if I could tell you we extended our honeymoon for the full four days in a beautiful part of the country, but alas we decided that this was the ideal time to operate on the Crossley.

We reluctantly closed our caravan door and set off for home. This being a Friday, we were due to return to the farm on Monday so milking could start on Tuesday morning. It meant that our decision to better the Crossley car had to be accomplished in four days and we yet had to find a more powerful engine as well as fit it into the

2

chassis. We had saved £5 towards this conversion and this had to be enough to finance the job. It may seem quite a big undertaking by today's standards but we had some things in our favour: I had a good relationship with our local car breaker, and the workshop where I had been repairing tractors before our marriage and starting to work for Alfa Laval still existed on my father's farm. So we took up residence with my parents and, hitching the car trailer to the back of the Crossley, I set off for our friendly car breaker's yard.

It was a desperately cold day and in truth the thought of working out in the open on an old car did not appeal at all. But it had to be done. After about an hour of inspecting old cars an engine was found that matched the measurements I had with me and that looked as if it could be fitted into our car. It was an Austin 14/6. Although it was about two inches longer than the existing engine it seemed to be the best available, and a deal was struck that meant if I would take it out myself the cost would be £1 5s. By this time my enthusiasm for the job was growing with the vision of us soaring up steep hills propelled by a more powerful six-cylinder engine, even if it was a side-valve unit and not renowned for high performance.

I suppose that to modern mechanics, used to computer-controlled diagnostic equipment and ultra-clean and warm working conditions, it may seem strange and very difficult to believe that someone could work outside in icy conditions with a mixture of oil and mud underfoot. It may also seem unbelievable to today's generation of engineers, trained to work to fractions of a millimetre, that anyone could contemplate engineering changes of this magnitude to be undertaken with a one-foot ruler, a hammer and an assortment of spanners – but I have to tell them that when my livelihood is threatened these things come naturally.

After about an hour's work the engine and gearbox were ready to lift out of the old car. That job was beyond me and anyway my fingers had departed for the North Pole, so off I went to the workers' hut to warm my fingers and myself on the little coal-fired stove I knew would be glowing red inside. After some banter about people 'skiving' by hot stoves whilst others had to work out in the cold it was explained to me that the price for scrap was now high enough to make it worthwhile to break up some of the many old cars in the yard and raise some much-needed cash. The procedure would be to set fire to a car, thus clearing all the wood and upholstery from the metal and then just cut it into handleable chunks . . . So if they helped me to lift out my engine would I help them roll a few cars into a circle so the fire stage could begin?

Once this was agreed my engine and gearbox were carried to the trailer. No one said 'You have not paid for the gearbox,' so, as I hoped, it was left fastened to the engine. We rolled a few cars into a circle, then selected one with some wheels on it and moved it into the centre of the 'burning-ground'. With damp upholstery it proved difficult to fire so it was rolled over and a chisel put through the fuel tank lower end, the resulting mixture of rusty petrol and water thrown into the car and lit with a cutting torch. We had a lovely warm fire with masses of black smoke climbing towards the sky. As it rose on the clear frosty air powered by about six feet of bright red flame, someone in a nearby office must have seen this pall of smoke and called the fire brigade, because with a clanging of bells a bright red fire tender arrived in the gateway and six firemen jumped out and began to run out

4

hosepipes. The car breaker looked on in amazement for a few seconds before going over to ask what they were doing. Attending that fire, he was told, 'Nay lad,' the breaker said, 'if you want a fire go and find your own bloody fire – this one is mine!'

JIM ECKERSLEY

With the fire tender away in search of its own fire or back to the fire station, the gateway was clear for me to drive away with our 'new' engine. As I drove home my thoughts were on the job ahead, having bargained for the engine at the price of £1 5s. No one had mentioned the gearbox, starter, dynamo, carburettor or ignition distributor. These units were still fixed to the engine riding home happily in the trailer, so our £1 5s had bought a great deal and we still had £3 15s left. The Austin engine was unloaded, accessories removed, and clutch checked. Washed down with paraffin and afterwards sprayed with a water hose, the engine now looked quite sparkling, especially the aluminium bits. The starter needed new armature brushes but I had a box of these and with a little help from a file that problem was soon remedied. What I did not do (and this was a fundamental mistake) was to take the engine to pieces. But time was short – there were only three days left to fit the engine and return to Elijah.

The Coventry Climax engine powered the car into our workshop, taking up a position under the pulley block and filling the doorway with motor car. Betty and I were inside and not able to pass the car to get out. We attached the lifting gear to the engine, disconnected the ancillary equipment including fuel pipes and electric fuel pump, which spilled petrol liberally around, and started to lift out the engine. In my hurry I had forgotten to take off the main electric lead to the starter which promptly caught on the chassis, giving off blue flashes of electricity. The spilled petrol failed to catch fire, or this story might never have been written. We could have been barbecued and the firemen might then have had a real fire to attend. I have worked on many tractors and cars since that date and have never forgotten to remove the battery leads before doing anything to them. So remember, safety first!

The Austin engine fitted quite well: two pads on the clutch casing mated with two pads on the Crossley chassis, rubber blocks were made from conveyor belting and the rear of the engine was in place. The crank 'V' pulley caught on the front chassis member but I bent the member upwards with my pipe wrench and all was well; a milking machine pipeline hanger bracket was cut and drilled to make two front engine mounts and the engine was in place; another day's work and the wiring loom was made, transmission drive line reworked and fuel lines made. We were ready for a trial. We had a new exhaust silencer made from $1\frac{1}{2}$ inch steel tube with 1 inch steel tube inlet and outlet pipes. (I can just see sometime in the future a heap of rust that used to be a car but with an almost new exhaust system that has stood the ravages of time . . .)

Our journey back to Elijah's farm was quite an adventure with the smooth six-cylinder engine and the thrill of its extra performance but I did become concerned about the blue haze following us around, especially in Melton Mowbray where it hung between the shops like a fog. Luckily the traffic lights were at green so we did not have to stop to see if the shoppers were coughing. The engine turned out to be a real old oil boiler but I did manage to find a set of new pistons and rings to fit and two weeks later, on a Sunday (the better the day the better the deed), we fitted them and our oil problem was cured.

As we settled down life began to get more hectic. For some reason Alfa Laval expected me to do a full week's work. I suppose this was not unreasonable as they were paying my wages. As the nights became lighter there was more work available repairing tractors on the farms we were visiting; also my father was experiencing machinery problems at home – David Brown was difficult to start and our old open crank engine almost impossible, so Betty and I were to be found at least one day each weekend grinding corn or repairing the farm machinery. There were also many enquiries about cultivation work and tractor repairs coming to my father from past customers who had been the mainstay of my income from the days before we were married.

One day in early summer we had a thunderstorm. This proved too much for our caravan roof, which was of proofed canvas but obviously no longer waterproof. We spent a happy hour trying to catch water before it ruined too many of our things. Anyway we had to do something – neither of us could swim! Seeking advice, we were told to paint the roof with Bostick and when dry give it a coat of silver paint. The Bostick was applied and we had a caravan roof coated with a dark grey rubberised substance which when dry would be painted with Alfa Laval bright silver pipeline paint. It never crossed my mind that whilst applying the Bostick in hot sun I was inhaling more solvent fumes than some of today's misguided yobs do with a stack of glue cans and half an acre of plastic bags. Betty and I lived in our 'solvent box' for several days before the smell went away. We survived with never a thought about any dangers this funny smell had.

Our next job took us to Market Bosworth to a farm owned by a late-middle-aged farmer we knew as Jack. He was a wonderful character, capable of working really hard when under pressure but also capable of complete lethargy when the pressure was off. When not moving at a gallop he could tell the most wonderful tales of 'the old days'. My own working day on his farm closely followed his. He would rush off in the morning, down the fields, or to market, perhaps to borrow something from a neighbour; I would work hard with the intention of getting the job done quickly, but alas when he returned work slowed to a stop whilst yet another tale was told. I imagined my supervisor in the Alfa Laval office in Brentford might be turning in his desk (I cannot say grave because he was very much alive) as the various documents reaching me urged more application to the job and stressed how many machines behind we were and how the customers were getting restless.

One of Jack's stories I will relate in spite of my vow not to write anything I had not experienced. Jack's character gave me some confidence that his stories were mostly true, so here goes for the only tale in this book not verified by me.

On one side of the farmyard was a rather neat apple tree beautifully proportioned in a mushroom shape. I remarked on its shape and so sparked Jack off. He called it

8

the sparrow tree. It appears that when the harvest was being carried into the barn (by horse and harvest wagon, of course, in those days) ready for threshing, there was always an accumulation of chaff, corn and a few ears of corn broken off the sheaves and lying in the bottom of the harvest wagons. Jack's father would give instructions that this debris should be spread under that particular tree so the hens could do a little foraging of their own and thus not waste this bounty; it also attracted many birds, predominantly the common house sparrow. The corn etc. was thrown under the tree in the late afternoon when the wagons were empty and being parked for the night. There was obviously much activity around and under the tree at this time and as hens retired to the hen house, many sparrows simply perched in the tree, all well fed.

After the harvest and at a time decreed by Jack's dad, all hands would be summoned after dark to cast a net over the tree — no doubt as we often see people casting large nets into a river when fishing. I have seen the remains of the 'sparrow net' gently rotting in his barn. The net was lightly weighted on one side so it would carry over the tree and fine enough to seal the sparrows inside. I was told a windless and moonlit night was usually chosen for this harvest. Using a ladder of the correct length or just climbing up the tree, it was reasonably easy to catch the terrified netted birds. Each as it was caught had its neck pulled and was then dropped into a bucket. Why was this done? Well, apparently the tradition was started by Jack's grandfather, who must have been quite a local character. He would provide for the workers a harvest supper part of which was, by tradition, a sparrow pie. There were of course many other country dishes with locally brewed beer and other drinks.

The morning after the harvesting of the sparrows (Jack

estimated there might be as many as two hundred in buckets) the farm ladies would take each sparrow corpse, scald it in boiling water, quickly remove, pluck the feathers, cut off the head and feet, slit the carcase and remove the unwanted inner parts with a sharp knife and a finger, then drop the body in a bucket of salted water whilst the farm cats squabbled amongst themselves for the pleasure of eating the discarded giblets. After washing these tiny but, in early autumn, plump bodies they would boil them in buckets of water. (I wonder if these were the same buckets that would be used in the afternoon milking? I expect they were.) After the sparrows were parboiled they were placed in a large pan, legs uppermost, crusted over with pie crust and cooked in the farm oven. In a particularly good year for the sparrow crop they would be cooked in a larger pan in the baker's oven. Can you imagine the barn floor brushed clean, the workers sitting at rough scrubbed tables with the sparrow pie as a traditional opener and probably another meat, vegetables, fruit, plenty of ale and maybe a local fiddler for the after-dinner entertainment? Was Jack kidding me? I do not think so but you must make up your own mind on this one.

Alas, I have never seen Jack again. I wonder how long he used the milking machine. His standard of hygiene varied with his feelings and as to how busy he might be on a particular day. One day the machine would be cleaned to perfection, another the teat cups would have a quick rinse with half a gallon of water drawn through them, then left until Jack came back from market or whatever urgent mission had taken him away from the farm. As often as not he would only return in time for the afternoon milking so there was no time to wash up the morning milk things before they were back on the cow and at work again, and that day there was no sterilisation of the milk equipment. It was up to me to make sure that all operators knew how important this job was, but my faith in everyone doing it after my departure left grave doubt in my mind in some cases. Since those days I have never fancied drinking raw milk.

2

AS time went on my father experienced more and more mechanical difficulties until it became plain to see that if he was going to lead a peaceful life – or Betty and I have any weekends when we were not working on machinery – we should again have to pool our respective skills, my father providing the animal husbandry whilst I could operate and repair the machinery. We knew this and all agreed it was the way to go but as the acreage was not large enough to support our ambitions we had to carry on as we were for the time being.

Our next milking machine job was in north Derbyshire at a village called Chelmorton on a farm owned by the local butcher. This almost started as a public-relations disaster. Our caravan was normally sited in a field or the farm orchard but here it was to rest in the farmyard. Our wonderful drainage system for washing ourselves or the pots simply went through a piece of milking machine tubing to the nearest ditch, our site being carefully chosen for this purpose. But in the farmyard it represented a problem. We had a chemical toilet so this waste was no problem at all to us but the washing water most definitely was. However, I sited the caravan by a large heap of firewood and ran our drainpipe into the middle of it and hoped the water would soak into the ground. It did but right through the ventilator and into the cold room where the stock of meat was stored. The next morning our attention was drawn to this disaster by a vexed butcher ... Telegrams to my employer, poisoned villagers, health inspectors, council officials, department of health representatives, even the gallows or a firing squad flashed through my mind; but after we finished mopping up around the sides of beef and other meats he gave us two nice steaks and so we were probably forgiven. We now were provided with an old milk churn to run our waste into so we could empty it down the farm drains.

Some time later – probably July 1950 – a local farmer who was having machinery and labour problems agreed we should undertake his whole machinery operation. Betty found work in our local corn merchant's office so I gave Alfa Laval my notice to quit and returned to my original workshop and tractor work at Ambaston. Looking after our new customer's cultivation work and indeed our own field work meant that our eighteen-month honeymoon travelling and working for Alfa Laval was over. Betty and I now entered one of the most active parts of our life; so much so that, whilst I can feel reasonably confident of events before and after this period, it is very difficult for me to cross my heart and swear that events during the period 1950 to 1956 are in true chronological order. Betty was making new friends at work whilst we were able to hold our relationship with the friends we had had over many war and post-war years. I remember with great pleasure our friends Bob and Hazel Trowel, Jo and Terry, our membership of the Ilkeston and District motor cycle club, and the many people we met there, all these good people contributed a great deal to our life and enriched it with the experiences and humour we shared in the early fifties.

Our caravan home took up position in the farmyard, quite close to the corn-grinding shed where the open crank engine and mill lived. We had a hard-standing base with flower borders around it, mains drainage and electricity with a water tap on site. My mother cultivated the flower borders with all the skill and love of flowers that she possessed. We may have still been tight for money but love and a pleasant life-style made up for most deficiencies. As time went on we even had a rented 12-inch television set. Betty cycled off to Shardlow every day to her work at 9 am, cycling the two miles home for a midday meal, usually prepared by Granny Hardy, so her cycling amounted to eight miles per day in all weathers. She often remarks on this period of her youth as being the fittest of her life.

I was involved in restoring David Brown to good health. The rest he had experienced during my absence from the farm had left him a little asthmatical, needing a valve job and set of piston rings fitted; it was also time to apply a coat of hunting pink paint so we could present a businesslike appearance when working for customers on their farms. After a few days' work we had a smart tractor breathing well and using no oil.

To further bolster our income we had to become much more productive on our farm. To this end we looked closely at egg production. This was a fashionable thing to do at this time but in common with many of the Government's policies it was badly thought through, farmers and smallholders being encouraged to invest quite large sums of money in buildings, fittings, usually battery laying-cages and highly bred stock; then they needed to buy expensive feeds to ensure high egg production and healthy birds; this left profit margins extremely thin or nonexistent, so many people who just trusted the Government figures lost a lot of money before their education was completed or, as others did, just gave up. I was different. My experience of the dreaded Warag (War Agricultural Committee) had left me a doubter of official-dom's capabilities in business acumen, so we looked a little deeper into most projects, especially if promoted by the Government and most especially so if it should be a socialist one – it being my opinion they could not organise a party in a brothel.

Our poultry building we found at the site of an old army camp. I had heard of Nissen huts going cheap in Boulton Lane near to us where the council intended to build a new housing estate, so off we went to view. The huts were quite large, about 40 feet long and 18 feet wide, and they represented good value for money as far as cheap cover went. However, upon looking further we saw a Romney hut with side windows, lined with plaster board and fitted out as a mess-room, complete with sinks, interior brick walls, and floored with concrete slabs. This, also available for £25, was 120 feet long and 24 feet wide. The only problem was that it had to be dismantled and the site cleared in two weeks. My natural greed and an unfailing belief in my own capabilities pressurised father into agreeing the purchase. We had one hell of a job to clear it in the time allowed, but I persuaded Uncle Chess, my great helper in previous years who had ridden the binder during our harvesting operations (see *Early Years*, p.102) to assist and by working every available daylight hour we moved it. Our David Brown tractor was never so busy, carrying not only the hut but many loads of bricks from the walls we had to remove. These we simply pushed over by reversing the trailer into them and then loading the bricks for transport. Afterwards he dressed the thousands of bricks and so we had not only a poultry shed but all the bricks to build the walls to mount it on, also a floor and a lined shed enough to hold hundreds of battery laying-cages. I may add it took considerably longer to rebuild it than it did to take it down but even so it was a very cheap solution to our poultry house requirement. Of course we had no planning permission to build such a large shed in our orchard but we did not dwell on small things like that in those days.

With our Romney hut ready for use we needed hen battery cages. We had decided on a battery system as opposed to running a deep-litter system, believing we could keep the hens healthier and avoid such problems as feather-plucking and 'bullying' or egg-eating etc. I now renewed my friendship with a man who was a customer of the garage where I had originally worked after leaving school, Arthur Millington by name. He was now making hen battery cages at relatively low cost, so by using a little cash and spending hours repairing his motor vehicles we became the proud owners of enough cages to hold five hundred hens. I had always believed the best production could be obtained from having cages that held only one bird, so all our birds were housed singly, and Millington's cages were built on this principle. I respected his experience in this, as he had been involved in poultry for most of his life. We had always called him Millington, never using his Christian name. He had originally arrived in Draycott as poultry manager to a gentleman whose name was Longdon. Mr Longdon had a rather unusual car which we serviced for him. It was a Hillman Hawk, a prototype for the Humber staff cars used during the war years by the army. This car would stop outside the garage and whilst I was filling it with petrol I could clearly hear Mr Longdon shouting into the garage 'Have you seen Millington today?' and this form of address just seemed to stick, he was 'Millington' ever after.

The Austin car Millington owned at this time was a car of character. Not fast – it would have grave difficulty achieving 60 mph downhill with a following wind – but it was so smooth and quiet; inside there was real leather

16

upholstery which was soft and comfortable; in the rear compartment was a cocktail cabinet and if one sat correctly in the seat and stretched one's legs forward it was impossible to reach the back of the front seats. I was allowed to use this car due to the hours' labour involved in rebuilding its six-cylinder 16 hp engine which gave over 30 mpg, which at that time was exceptionally good. On Friday nights it was reserved for the use of a young unmarried (I think) man who helped build the battery cages. Friday night was the one night in the week he never worked, but apparently took a young lady out on the town. Some weeks after the car's first outing with this young man it returned on the Saturday morning with obvious signs of the rear compartment having been fully used, i.e. a pair of lady's knickers in the rear door pocket. Millington's response was immediate: 'I see you have been using the owd Austin as a palace of fornication.' Ever after the car was known to us all as the 'Fornicatorium'. It bore its new name with grand indifference, running just as sweetly as ever.

Whilst we are talking about our friend Millington, I recall some years earlier the very first car I ever filled up with petrol at the garage. It was an Austin 12 owned by him. In those days the petrol pump had a large glass bowl sitting on top of the pump. One moved a lever along a slot to the position marked with the required quantity to be sold and pumped the hand lever until the petrol was delivered to the glass bowl then turned the hand lever on the end of the hose and allowed the petrol to run by gravity into the fuel tank, afterwards lifting the hose and draining the last drops into the tank. If the driver was not of the aware type one never drained the hose and so had a couple of pints left in it for recovery later for one's own use. Millington's Austin car was known as a fabric saloon, in other words a wooden body not panelled with metal but covered with canvas stretched and shaped to the contours. These bodies were considered a step up on the normal car but tended to suffer wear and tear to the canvas. This Austin was no exception, Millington had purchased it from the car breaker, the one described previously, for the princely sum of £2 10s as a runner. It ran for the next six months on his egg round and other journeys until it broke down and was taken back to the breaker and changed for a rather splendid Rover 10, the astronomical sum of £5 also being involved.

During our battery cage deal Millington came to tell me of a Bedford van he had bought. It seems strange how he and I were always involved in vehicle escapades . . . The Bedford van had belonged to a speedway rider who used it to carry his two machines around, riding up to four meetings each week in the racing season. This was a very hard life. Our local team, Long Eaton, was in the second division and had to travel as far as Edinburgh or to the far south of England. This meant that after a meeting had finished the journey home would be started at around 10.30 pm and could be as far as two hundred miles. Riders had a small retainer paid by the team promoter but made up most of their earnings at the rate of £5 for each heat they started in, up to five each night and £5 for each point scored at 3 for a win, 2 for second, and 1 for third place. In such a competitive sport high income was hard to come by and hotel expenses were to be avoided, so to save money the journey home would as often as possible be made after the meeting. The journey home might be a wonderful drive if a good night's earnings had been achieved; but if the rider had had a crash and was feeling bruised and battered or the machine was damaged and it was foggy then he might be asking himself why he was doing this. Cuts and bruises usually heal quickly and at low cost but bikes cost a lot to repair.

On one of these hectic return journeys the Bedford van had run over a garden hedge, demolished a wall and sat in solitary confinement on someone's front lawn. Attempts to reverse off had resulted in two neat holes being dug by the rear wheels which must have further infuriated the gardener, so the next morning Millington, who perhaps had a more than passing aquaintance with the driver, agreed to tow the van out of the garden with the Fornicatorium. With its power and weight presented to the van and with the van tied on the end of a rope, and a few bricks cleared away which the headlong career of the van had spread around the previous night, a little Austin power was applied and the van was back on the highway. Very little damage had been done to the van. It was driven away and the Austin followed, we cannot say in hot pursuit, it being a very laid-back car which did nothing hot or fast except perhaps to provide certain young bloods with hot assignation accommodation; anyway, after a mile or so the van was spied standing on the side of the road, due, our speedway friend said, to all the big ends having failed. So the van was again tied on to a rope and towed away, the bikes were delivered to the speedway track and the van left in Millington's yard waiting for the car breaker to collect it.

Looking around the van had convinced Millington of its inherent soundness so he bid the speedway laddie £10 for it and it was towed to Ambaston for me to repair the engine. This suited me − I could see a few more hen battery cages arriving in the near future. Looking around the van I found the engine oil sump had been severely pushed in by the crash. On removing the sump I found that the oil pick-up pipe had been broken and thus the oil

19

had not been fed to the engine, so the big end rattle had been caused by the lack of oil. Those old cars could survive a little problem like that; today's rubbish would have needed hospital care for a week to get over it. Repairing the pick-up pipe and bashing the sump into approximate shape enabled me to telephone Millington to say his van was ready for collection . . . and another block of hen battery cages arrived in our poultry house.

Our hen battery system was now making good progress and we were about to receive our first batch of day-old chicks. A brooder, self-watering system, and food troughs were made and the first 100 yellow little bundles of feathers took up residence. Using infrared lamps for warmth we raised 98 of our first 100 chicks. From then onwards we received 100 chicks per week until we had 600 in all. My Alfa Laval experience with milking machinery was put to good use arranging water and drainage for our new venture. Since it was mainly I who would have to do the work you may be sure no effort was spared to make everything as easy as possible. A dripping tap gave us a kind of automatic drinking system whilst all the droppings were drawn from under the birds and into a wheelbarrow ready to carry away to the muck heap. With our old engine and mill producing ground corn and with the supplements we bought in, a good poultry mix was fed to our hens; this with a really efficient ventilation system we had arranged in our battery house made sure we did not suffer from the usual smells, feather-plucking and general bad health so many of the intensive systems suffered from at that time. I well remember the wet, bedraggled and cold hens wandering around the farmyard looking miserable and producing considerably fewer eggs per year than our warm, well-ventilated and healthy hens in the battery shed. I laugh to myself when I read of some well-intentioned criticism of a hen battery system from people who perhaps see happy hens running free in a buttercup meadow under a nice bright sun – I have to tell them life is only like that on rare occasions.

If you feel I dwell on poultry too much it is because I was proud of our hen unit and its above-average production. But tractors and field work were my main job. We were still doing cultivation work for other farmers.

One day we had a call from a customer about six miles away to plough a field of ley. (This is a plough field sown with grass seed usually for one or two years before it is again ploughed, usually after a hay crop has been taken from it, and is prepared for a winter crop to be planted.) In late July I drove David Brown into the field only to find it populated with cows. This was not of any concern to me as it was my belief that the farmer would come to fetch them at milking time, so a headland mark was drawn around the field, a ridge drawn together, and ploughing commenced. Intending to mark the rest of the field out when the cows had been removed so they would not eat the stick used for measuring out the area to plough, I had been round the ploughing two or three times. This had the cows quite excited: they responded as cows so often do by sticking their horns into the newly turned furrows and throwing them around. Here was I trying to get the whole field brown side up and the cows were trying to get it back to green again. I figured if the farmer had no more sense than to leave cows in a field when it was being ploughed he would just have to stand the cost of an extra pass with the disc harrow to correct the mess his stock had made. Anyway I was being paid not by the hour but by the acre, so it was imperative to press on with the job. I was not about to stop for a few cows. Then I saw him – a young and quite mobile bull.

21

Now we had a bull at home about the same age as this one and he and I definitely did not get on together. We had a particularly nasty set-to one day. Usually my father would turn him out into the yard each day whilst he cleaned out the stall, water bowl and manger. This afforded Bill some exercise, whilst my mother watched he did not get too playful and break something. Mother used to talk to him and often take him a handful of nice fresh grass, so she was the apple of his eye. I usually ignored him, as he could be controlled quite well by Mother; he had respect for her. I was another matter. In his eye I could read the thought in his head that he would get that ignorant young so-and-so even if he got turned into mincemeat for it. The right occasion arrived one day and he advanced towards me, head lowered threateningly. I of course was terrified but tried not to show it and in a low and I hoped threatening voice told him where to go and lectured him about his parentage. He just advanced smoothly towards me. I knew it would be fatal to run so I applied a liberal amount of pitchfork tine to and around his nose. This stopped him and he retreated. My father came to the rescue and Bill retired to his stall 'injured'. This did nothing for our relationship, which from that day forward could only be described as strained.

The young bull in the plough field, very active and threatening, helped his ladies tear up the furrows for a short while but as the tractor advanced along the furrow he turned and looked, pranced towards it, bounced away and eventually advanced again. I was most definitely unhappy and looked for the nearest gap in the hedge where I might get away. I felt exposed because David Brown was not wearing his bonnet sides (we were beginning to get overheating problems, so they had been left off). The bull approached from the land side of the field. I stood up on the footplate, waved my arms, and shouted in a language most dictionaries would not understand. He did not understand either and just kept on advancing. He gave the front wheel a good old thump with his head. Returning, he had another go and caught the side of the engine. But now the tractor bit back: as he butted the engine he caught the exposed magneto, shattering the coil cover; this stopped it sending sparks to the spark plugs but as the engine momentum ran down it managed to jolt our bull with a series of strong ignition shocks before the engine finally stopped. A most surprised bull shook his head, emitted a wounded '*burr*', and retired across the field. I sat in silence for a few seconds, then, realising David Brown was now dead and the bull about fifty yards away but very much alive, I departed for a fence in the hedge taking 'large strides and often', as we say in the country.

David Brown was now out of action so whilst we awaited a new coil cover the radiator was taken off and cleaned out in an attempt to stop the overheating that had begun to trouble us. At that time we never used anti-freeze in our engines so they were sometimes filled from dubious sources when the tractor was left in a field overnight during the winter. I know everyone will tell me you must not use ditchwater in tractor cooling systems but often it was a case of 'do as you can', not 'do as you should'. The overheating problem had caused the engine to overheat on a journey I had made just north of Derby to deliver some corn we had sold. The engine overheated very badly climbing a hill. After freewheeling down the other side an investigation showed the water level in the radiator had decreased so much it was not visible. Stopping the engine to allow it to cool down, I looked around for salvation . . . No house or farm within sight, not even a ditch. It seemed I was in for a long walk, but then an idea came to me. Seeing a surface-water drain on the roadside, I wondered whether there was water down there. *Yes*, water was shimmering at the bottom; so after prising the cover up and using an old tin used for carrying oil I was able to fill the radiator with a dark-coloured fluid which had possibly been clean rain-water once. David Brown restarted and I drove away complacently. But after two miles or so my mind was changed. The smell from the steam gently chuffing from the radiator cap was really unbelievable – a mixture of septic tank and manure from a pig farm, over which hung a suggestion of gents' toilet uncleaned for several days in a heatwave. Anyway I arrived home, but what did the population at large think was being carried in the trailer as I drove through Derby?

To clean out a vehicle radiator is quite a simple

procedure. After removing it from its seat, working on a clean surface turn the radiator upside down, pour water into the hole where the bottom hose fits (now at the top) and allow water to run through until it runs clean. To check if the radiator is blocked turn it the correct way up, fill with the hose, holding your hand over the bottom outlet; when the radiator is full take your hand away and note if the water runs out freely. Any sign of gurgling or bubbling probably means the radiator core is not flowing to full capacity and needs professional attention. (There are of course many good companies who will repair a radiator for you much more professionally but who charge the best part of a lot of money for the service.) Our radiator seemed to be quite clear so I started looking around for other problems. Checking the water pump and removing it from the tractor showed a V-shaped water tube running through the cylinder head. This was blocked and fell to pieces when it was removed (so, if you experience overheating on an old David Brown tractor, remember this). No replacement was easily available so it was never replaced. The tractor never boiled again.

3

ABOUT this time Granny Hardy's sister arrived on the scene, her husband, Uncle Jim, having retired from working in the Birmingham area where Granny's family came from. Aunt Ester her sister must have had good memories of the early years of this century when the family would visit Derbyshire for their holidays and thus decided this would be a good place to retire to. In the early 1920s many of her family working in the iron trade in Birmingham had their annual holiday during the first week in August, so many nieces, nephews, aunts, uncles etc. came to visit Granny and Grandad at Ambaston where he worked on a farm. They lived in the village in a farm cottage with one living room and one bedroom, so an influx of ten or twelve relations for the annual holiday presented quite a problem! But transport did not seem a problem: some came on bicycles, others took a train from Birmingham to Derby, changing for Borrowash station and taking the mile-and-a-half footpath along the riverside to Ambaston, carrying their holiday luggage with them. All would arrive within half a day of leaving home – travel is no quicker today.

After working in factories or shops in the Birmingham area, Ambaston with its quiet ways and slow pace of life must have seemed like heaven to those relatively poor people – no large salaries in those days. The main attractions were good country air, sunshine, and a gravel bed on the river Derwent just near the village where good bathing was available. How the sun always managed to shine on them every year I will never know but Granny

26

always insisted it did. If you are wondering how this great clan of happy people managed to fit into such a small house, it was quite simple: the ladies slept upstairs and the men in the living room downstairs or under a stack sheet borrowed from the farm and slung between the house and coal shed. It was here too that most of the meals were taken. Beds were made from sacking sewn to size and stuffed with clean straw. (This was burnt after the holiday and the sacking washed and saved for next year.) Cooking was mostly done on the coal range in the house, which also heated about two gallons of water; but the main supply of hot water was the old copper, also coal-fired and situated in the wash house, usually used for washing clothes but now pressed into service to boil water for more personal washing as well as for boiling large batches of potatoes, or, if funds allowed, a whole ham to feed the hungry horde. Evening entertainment was walking, especially in the direction of the Harrington Arms in the next village.

After living in several other houses during the 1930s Granny was back in the little cottage and her return probably sparked happy memories in Aunt Ester, as she eventually found a small cottage in the next village, at the end of Ambaston Lane in Shardlow. This was part of a terrace of five cottages with a reasonable-sized garden and she and Uncle Jim settled down quite well in their new surroundings. All would have been well but as many people do they decided a dog would complete their retirement and give some point to walking up the lane in true country style, as they saw it. I do not remember where he came from but he must have cost quite a pile of money, because this small bundle of black fur arrived with a pedigree as long as a wet week, decreeing him to be a cocker spaniel. All went well whilst he grew for a few weeks; Aunt Ester got him house-trained eventually after the usual disasters; Uncle Jim made him a kennel from a tea chest which was placed under the kitchen sink.

A few weeks later it was a different story. Rex – the name came from his pedigree and was the first part of a long name some of which was unpronounceable – had grown. Now a large puppy with unbounded energy, he was proving to have more pulling power than either Aunt Ester or Uncle Jim could handle. After collecting skinned knees and gravel-rashed hands they gave up trying to take him for a walk on the lead. He was only allowed off the lead once. Proving deaf to all calls for him to return he eventually came home after four hours' freedom, and never went off the lead again. Some of the local children were bribed to take him for a walk but he spent more time in his tea-chest kennel than ever. The so-called kennel was now much too small for him so his energy increased as the space available to him decreased. Each day he was let out at tea time for his evening meal. This was a sight to behold as Rex raced around the house like an express train round the chairs, between the old people's legs, up the settee and over the back, scattering rugs and small pieces of furniture. I think Aunt Ester originally thought of herself sitting in an armchair with Rex on her knee being gently stroked. But that was before he arrived: the reality was quite a shock.

One day I called at the house to find that Rex could now jump from the settee to the top of the sideboard and, having scattered and broken some ornaments, was in some disgrace. I was asked if I would take him to the RSPCA to be put down as they had decided he was 'wrong in the head', because he was impossible to train. Strong talking and beating had no effect on him. Aunt Ester decided he was too inbred.

It seemed such a shame that a lovely dog like Rex should be just simply killed. I suggested I try to quieten him myself, an offer which was quickly taken. I was told to either keep him or take him to be put down. He was escorted to the car, my father's Citroën Rosalie, and tied to the gear lever to stop him jumping all over me during the journey home. My father and mother had of course seen all the trials and tribulations Aunt Ester had suffered with him and so were not surprised to see him arrive at Brook Farm.

You will remember the Romney hut we bought and used one end for the battery hens. Well, the other was unused except for some straw bales. Rex was taken into that half and released, where he jumped around and yapped for joy. The shed became not a greyhound track but a spaniel track. Round and round he went so we left him to it. Four hours later he was still running, but slower, and I decided we had found the answer. The next morning he was still very active so we gave him water and left him another day and night. The following day he would come to me when I called his name and allow himself to be stroked. We had no more trouble from him. He followed me into the house and had a meal for the first time in two days and then slept on the hearthrug with the cats. It was most surprising how well they agreed together, just a growling complaint from Rex or a hiss from a cat if they lay on one another. In the winter with the fire well banked up a cinder might roll off to be followed by the smell of scorched fur and, as fur gave way to flesh, the inevitable mêlée of animals scrambling for safety and the struggle to establish themselves in a new and warm position as they returned, each to his favoured piece of hearthrug. It was at this time that my father developed a heavy cold, not improved by his insistence to carry on working. One evening while he was sitting in his favoured armchair one of the cats, a tortoiseshell lady which for some reason not now clear to me was graced with the name 'Shake', arrived on his knee as was her custom. With blocked nose and streaming eyes he was in the habit of sniffing a bottle of smelling salts to clear his congestion. As he was taking a strong sniff the cat lifted her head to look and almost unconsciously he offered her the bottle. Now this wily old creature really should have had more sense, but in fact took a strong sniff from the bottle – and all hell broke loose! She bounced straight up and over Father's head with a terrible howl leaving traction marks on his scalp as she disappeared down the back

JIM ECKERSLEY

of the chair to sit spitting with rage and discomfort at the back. The other cats scattered from the hearthrug in various directions whilst Rex spread himself, glad to have the fire to himself for once.

One of our local garages had been sold the previous year to the Esso Company. The original proprietor had retired to live on the outskirts of Nottingham, thinking no doubt how nice it was to have perpetual leisure. But after a while he had obviously tired of this so-called idyllic lifestyle and bought an agricultural machinery business, which among other things included the agency for Marshall tractors and Fisher Humphrey ploughs. He called me one day to see if I would help them set their demonstration plough as no one at the company knew anything about ploughing.

I was afterwards to find out that they had been severely thrashed when demonstrating the Marshall against a

Ferguson outfit, notwithstanding that the Marshall – costing more money and having much more power than the Ferguson – should have been well able to cope. Finally the Marshall had got bogged down and they had returned to the depot with their tail severely tucked between their legs.

Obviously this could not be allowed to happen again, especially as the Ferguson dealer had gone home with a cheque and proceeded to recount this triumphant episode around the local markets. I was supposed to help correct this situation. The need was urgent so the offer was a £5 note to go and set up the plough for them and attend the next day's demonstration to another farmer. It was a very tempting situation to me, not only for the £5 note but also because this kind of work appealed to me as an extension of the ploughing matches I competed in. It carried a similar challenge and involved the 'living on your wits' element that I so much enjoyed.

During the afternoon I arrived at the field described to me on the telephone to find the tractor and plough already on site. It was by my insistence that we had set up the equipment the day before the demonstration; they would have left it until the day of the event, even until arriving at the site. So no wonder they had failed so miserably on the previous occasion. I began to see how hopeless people could be who believed a plough, being so simple, would not be any problem. How little some people know! The plough, a four-furrow, was bigger than any I had ever used before. Luckily for me they said I need not bother about the tractor. They were Field Marshall specialists but were not too happy about plough settings or perhaps I should have been completely overawed.

The plough was new, all the earthmoving parts being

covered in preservative. Had they any paint-stripper? No, they said, but it will come off after a few yards. A quarter of a mile of ploughing later the preservative had not moved at all – the loose soil had not the abrasive character to remove it and the tractor was struggling to pull the plough. Just imagine getting into a wet field with that outfit! I was beginning to find out there was much more to demonstrating a tractor than I had realised, but I was gaining confidence as I found out that the people who were 'experts' probably had not enough skill to push a wheelbarrow, never mind demonstrate a tractor and plough.

A council of war was convened, the result of which was that one man was sent for paint-stripper whilst I provided a crash course in how to drive a tractor straight and how to ensure the plough was hitched correctly behind the tractor. I was learning in a hard school how many things can be wrong with a simple sales job. 'No wonder we failed at the last event,' they said, 'that plough did not clean either.' – 'That's another thing', I asked. 'How come you failed with three furrows and now we are involved with a four-furrow plough?'

'Ah well,' the owner said, 'when you agreed to come I knew it was worth an extra furrow.' Having known him a good number of years I could tell from his wicked smile I was being set up. It turned out that he had a new salesman who had glibly promised a local farmer that the Field Marshall would pull four furrows, the farmer's reaction having been, 'OK, prove it.'

By now I was beginning to enjoy myself, gaining confidence all the time and no longer feeling a farm boy amongst experts. We got the preservative off the plough, set up the disc coulters and skims, hitched it correctly behind the tractor and were producing quite good work, but still with too much wheel slip. I finally decided the experts were wrong again and we must reduce the tyre pressures. 'But we set them just as the book said,' protested the experts.

'Never mind, they are no good without some flex in the tyre walls,' I told them and proceeded to lower the pressures until there was enough flex to satisfy me. Now when tested the pressure read nine pounds per square inch. 'Excellent,' I said. 'Catastrophic,' said the experts. They were totally lost but after some explanation from me they began to learn about tyre performance and how vital it is to the good performance of a tractor. We now ploughed across the field with little wheel slip. The Marshall toured across the field with a crisp exhaust note, 'a road drill on wheels', as I like to call it. I was paid the £5 note and promised to attend the demonstration the next day at 10 a.m.

The next day was wet: we were wet, the field was wet, our competitors the Ferguson people were wet and all of us were getting wetter by the minute. The grey Fergie struggled to pull three furrows and we struggled to pull four furrows. The field had no stubble cover, just greasy and muddy soil. The farmer who had challenged us said he thought we might have problems; the owner remarked that we were going much better than last time out and certainly as well as the Ferguson despite our extra furrow. I could see the ground was not heavy and had very little clay in it so decided to try a different technique. The farmer looked on in disbelief. The Ferguson team smiled and said, 'Good ploughing is the basis of good farming.' I just carried on with my alterations, they did not know I was only doing what had been done over many years of contracting so the outfit could be kept at work in adverse conditions and keep the money rolling

34

in. The principle was to get the tractor moving faster, so the drawbar on the plough was lowered a little so it bore down on the tractor much more and pulled the rear wheels into the ground for better traction. Although this often means the work may be uneven, it can be disguised by the use of the levelling lever on the plough and the front furrow-width adjuster. The three front coulters were taken off and the skim coulter taken from the rear disc, which was left in place to give a nice clean furrow wall – there was no trash to bury so why pull skim coulters that are not needed?

The farmer and the Ferguson team gathered round to watch our failure to plough decently. I still felt confident and told the driver to use the highest possible gear; but he asked me to drive so off we went. After a short distance the plough presented good even work to the required depth but the Marshall no longer sounded like a road drill but now, in a high gear and the throttle well open, it sounded like an anti-aircraft gun on wheels: deep explosions from the exhaust, a plume of black smoke from the stack. We travelled up and down with little or no wheel slip, the land front wheel just lifting clear of the ground on occasion. The Ferguson team with much less power but a better weight transfer system were still struggling. They had been gently amused at my alterations. Surely now, they must have been thinking, we shall prove better; that plough cannot produce good work without those disc coulters and skims. They were disappointed that our plough now turned the ground over so quickly it was smashed into a good tilth just ready to drill, leaving no furrows that would need harrowing. It worked even better than I expected. But remember that the type of plough body on our plough was the International Ace body that I had been using for many years, so it was possible to guess what result would be achieved. The unknown factor was the Marshall's power, and this tractor produced more power than I could have forseen. How good to have a new tractor with plenty of power and be able to work it to the full potential of its engine!

The farmer and the dealership owner were very impressed but I must say the Ferguson people had to fall back on the story that their demonstration tractor was just as could be bought from stock and they never 'souped-up' the demonstrator. This was an ill-judged line to take as it gave the owner the opportunity to say that of course the Marshall was quite standard and to prove it the farmer could buy that very one if he wished. The next day a telephone call told me the Marshall and plough were being washed ready for delivery to the farmer and would I go over and prepare another one for demonstration. This was the first of many demonstrations, and the first of many £5 notes I earned both from the Marshall dealer and a Ford dealer some distance away.

For a long time I had been interested in a Field Marshall tractor, always believing increased profits were available if we could have more power, especially diesel power against the TVO power of our rather small David Brown tractor, but the price of a new Marshall had stopped me from making a change. We always seemed to be suffering an economic cramp of some kind but the demonstrations with a Marshall had cured me of this ambition in spite of its great power. I just could not see myself sitting on that thing for fourteen or sixteen hours a day whilst working on light jobs such as mowing or rolling and suffering the vibrations it produced when not working under power; I could see myself getting down from the footplate a temporary cripple . . . And what would dear Betty say then when her husband suffered reactions to this popping machine, especially if the reactions were carried on late into the night? We might even have ruined the bed springs and had to buy a new bed, all because of a Marshall tractor!

This decision about the Marshall was reinforced by an experience we had whilst helping a neighbour during a visit of the local threshing contractor. It was of course natural amongst all the local farmers to help one another during the threshing machine's visit. A large team was required and most farms just did not have a large enough labour force on their own, so each farm sent at least one man along to help, in the expectation that a return visit would be provided at the right time. These exchanges also provided a measure of your neighbour's successes or otherwise by putting a 'spy' in his camp, if only for a day or so. There was also the lady of the house, who provided the tea and meal for these extra workers; each lady would try and produce a wonderful feed just to show how well she could run her house. Only one farm did not rise to the occasion – the food was eatable (I suppose is the word) and the tea weak. Our farm worker when asked to go over there and help always described the tea brought out by the unmarried daughter as 'another drink of maidswater'. But this was the exception: we have mostly enjoyed wonderful food on these occasions.

The experience with the Marshall I refer to was probably caused to some extent by the owner or his driver using old sump oil to eke out the new diesel fuel poured into the fuel tank, although I have since seen the same thing happen when only new fuel was used. I was carrying and making a stack of bales just beyond the end of the baler. By mid afternoon with the sun shining, threshing machine humming nicely, dust and straw flying around and overall the fiendish hammering from a dirty oily

Marshall providing power and keeping us all on the run, I was about six layers of bales up the stack and so could sit on the top layer looking for the next bale to emerge from the baler when I noticed sparks out of the tractor exhaust pipe.

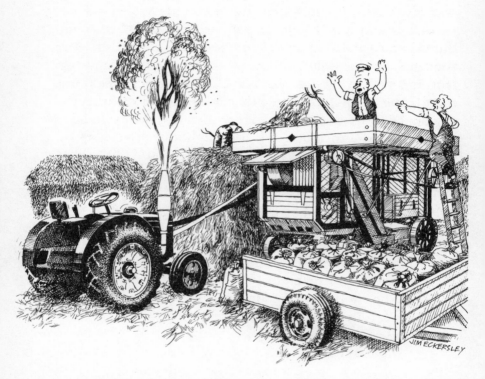

The Marshall gave a spirited impression of a mobile blowlamp.

Now sparks and straw and particularly dusty straw do not mix. It is only one step better than fire and gunpowder in my opinion. I shouted to the operator who was feeding the drum. He could not hear me for the 'gunfire' of the Marshall which quite unconcerned continued to hammer hell out of the afternoon air. So I ran to the drum, climbed the ladder until his attention could be drawn, and pointed to the Marshall. It was now doing a spirited impression of a firework on four wheels, flames flowing out of the exhaust pipe top, in fact it was a massive blowlamp, the flames shooting six feet out from the pipe and growing. The pipe was by now beginning to glow red even in the sunlight. The man ran to the tractor and shut down the engine. The flames continued to burn but now only gently with the occasional puff of flame and further showers of sparks. A wet sack was quickly found and thrown over the pipe. The fire ceased to be dangerous but it was a very dicey situation in a stackyard full of loose dry straw and other ricks.

Later the now cooled exhaust was removed and a large quantity of oily soot removed before we could carry on with our work . . . So my ambitions to own a Marshall took another turn.

4

IN 1951 or 1952 we were still working our David Brown quite hard and when not using it I was repairing tractors and cars, etc. in the workshop at Ambaston, which once housed the first car in our village, as Grandfather would remind me. About this time our landlord responded to the latest of many requests for some repairs to be done to the house, sketching out some changes which included an indoor flush toilet and, for the first time, the supreme luxury of a bathroom, so the old tin bath could be pensioned off. We were of course expected to pay more rent for this modernisation, but the worst thing was that this long-awaited event carried a sting in its tail. This was a request that we stop carrying out motor and tractor repairs on the farm because the farm rental agreement specifically stated this should not be done; the rates paid on farm property were agricultural and did not cover this type of work and we had to remember our landlord's agent was a county councillor and did not want an embarrassing situation to develop within the Derbyshire County Council. This particular pill was made sweeter for us to swallow because the landlord intimated that he would shortly be able to offer us another farm to help keep up our income level, so we could live from farming rather than tractor or vehicle repairs. I did not consider myself a farmer and was not too pleased with this decision but could do very little about it. We were offered the tenancy of Brook Farm in Thulston, a nearby village, so Mother and Father went to live there whilst Betty and I moved into Brook Farm, Ambaston –

our very first house, complete with new bathroom and flush toilet. All these changes meant we now had about 150 acres and still with plenty of machinery to run it and some time still to carry on with a few tillage contracts for neighbours. But we did need capital to increase our stock of mostly dairy cows.

There were some snags to this new arrangement. Two farms a mile apart are not the easiest units to run, especially since the Thulston farm only had about twenty acres near home, the rest of the land being alongside the main A6 trunk road a mile or so away. This was a very busy road indeed: there were no motorways in Britain at that time and the A6 was the main route from London to Manchester, on to Carlisle and then to Glasgow, so there was traffic night and day. The possibility of taking a milking herd along this road twice each day did not bear thinking about, but luckily in the past someone had built a simple milking shed to avoid this problem so the cows could stay away from home for the summer and the journey along the A6 with a herd of cows need only be made twice each year. Even so we had some exciting times when doing our dairy herd migration. It is surprising how fretful motorists can be when forced to travel at cow speed! We used the car and trailer in front of our herd with headlights on to hold the centre of the road whilst David Brown with large trailer held the centre of the road at the rear, stopping any one trying to overtake. We had longer lines of traffic than present–day cones on a motorway cause, but in spite of horns blowing and some shouted curses everyone had to wait.

The main farm buildings had a milking machine. This had been fitted by Fred (with whom I had experienced many adventures, as related in a previous book). But there was no milking machine in our temporary milking shed so it fell to me to fit one. As there was no electricity it would be necessary to use a small petrol engine to power the vacuum pump. We saw a Lister A type engine advertised in a farm sale. Possibly a Lister D would have been a better unit, but they were very costly at that time and difficult to obtain. We attended the sale and found the Lister marked as a 'good runner'. It had with it in the same lot a single-cylinder watercooled engine marked 'non-runner' which turned out to be a Villiers two-stroke engine of 1½ H.P. My father was reluctant to bid, he did not want two engines; but I persuaded him to do so, using the argument that the second engine could be bedded down at the main farm as a standby in case of electrical failure. So he bought both engines for £15.

We soon had the Villiers running and bedded down in a shed just adjacent to the cowshed to drive both the vacuum pump and a root-pulper as required. Using the Villiers each day to cut roots for mixing in the cows' feed ensured that it was always ready to start in case of electrical failure. A long exhaust pipe out into the open air produced an exhaust note like a Ferrari in a farmyard so it had to be silenced, but other than that it gave good service.

The Lister was a bigger job. We could not allow it to fail so I stripped it and did a rebuild on it to be sure Father could start it every day without fail. Often my day's work would start before his and if the engine had failed to start I would be away from home often at 5 or 5.30 am. If I was not working away from home Betty and I would not arise before 7.30 and, as we cherished those precious extra minutes of connubial bliss, it was not a welcome message to receive that the engine would not start.

With the pipeline fitted and the engine bedded down in our summer milking shed, it was time to start it and test the installation. The shed had a bottom half of brick construction with the top part of corrugated iron with an asbestos roof. As the engine not only had an exhaust that might awaken the dead but its resonance seemed to rattle every corrugated sheet on the shed, it seemed most unlikely that we should obtain any record milk yields from this unit. After I had tried various silencers without complete success, my friend the car breaker suggested that Rolls-Royce silenced their big engines by using a large expansion chamber as opposed to a baffle type silencer. Pondering on this I decided to make an expansion box. We had a supply of old milk churns with push-down lids. One of those would make a great expansion box, so the exhaust pipe was diverted into the side of the churn and an outlet went out the other side near the top, again using milking machine tubing; the top of the churn was pushed hard down into place; all the nails on the various sheets were hammered home to try and avoid the rattle being produced. When the engine was started, the difference was unbelievable: no exhaust note could be heard, one had to go outside and place one's ear to the pipe and then only a faint chuff could be heard every time the engine fired. The heaviest noise now was tappet rattle and the clack-clack of the belt fastener. My father could not believe it. •

Some weeks later we found the snag to our expansion chamber. There is usually a down side to any great breakthrough one may experience. This one emerged on a damp morning when the engine was reluctant to start and no doubt my father had partly choked the engine. After winding it for some time he had collected a milk churn full of unfired petrol mixture. By this time he left it for a few minutes to regain his breath then decided to have just one more go before calling me. One last good

43

sharp swing and it fired – so did the milk churn. My father described an immense explosion, a cloud of smoke along with a heavy sound of breaking asbestos, as the churn lid we had most carefully hammered down tight departed skywards. Space rocket engineers would have been proud of the effect. Straight through the asbestos roof and across the field it went. But as the engine was now running he milked a herd of trembling and apprehensive cows. From then on we only just lodged the lid on the churn without hammering it down. The backfire problem happened on other occasions but now it only dislodged the lid, there were no more space adventures. I can certainly recommend this system of silencing an engine . . . but for goodness' sake be careful and allow a pressure release system somewhere in the circuit.

Rex, our black cocker spaniel, had by this time settled in with us quite well but occasionally went missing until an urgent message was received from a neighbour. This usually ran along the lines that if we did not fetch our black horror from chasing his bitch he would shoot him. Now it so happened that we were due a visit from our vet so I decided to consult him about this problem, thinking he would suggest taking Rex into the surgery for a small operation. (I suppose we might regard it as small; what Rex would regard it as is another matter.) I mentioned the matter to the vet, expecting him to suggest making an appointment, but the answer was, 'OK, I have a few minutes to spare. We can do the job now if you wish. Is he likely to bite?'

'Possibly,' I replied cautiously. He asked for one of Betty's old nylon stockings, which we bound round Rex's muzzle. The vet then turned poor Rex over and, while I held him, produced a scalpel and expertly removed the cause of all the trouble.

'That will steady you, my lad,' said the vet. With his stocking removed, Rex walked unsteadily over to the hearthrug for a good lick.

The treatment worked: Rex became more house-bound and funnily enough more attached to me. When I went off to the other farm on the motor cycle he could be seen in full cry, ears flying in the wind, chasing me down the village yapping imploringly. Eventually I tried him on the fuel tank sitting on my knee just as Bruce had done in previous years. Rex like Bruce was a born motor cyclist, sitting on my knee with his front paws braced on the old sackbag I threw over the petrol tank. It was impossible to go too fast for him – I guess the maximum speed would be about 80 mph. Wet with rain or white with snow, Rex just had to go. Even heavy braking never dislodged him and around corners he could lean with the bike just as I did.

Our Scott motor cycle was now getting rather long in the tooth as it was a 1928 Super Squirrel model. However, spare parts were easy to obtain. For several years I had been buying them from a great Scott man, Tom Ward of Wilfred Street, Derby, now sadly departed for greener pastures without his Scott. Originally he had a motor cycle business in Hustler Street, Bradford (or as he pronounced it, Bratford). I was very keen on these twin-cylinder two-stroke motor cycles and eventually went to work for Tom three evenings a week. He was a first class and well qualified engineer who had arrived in Derby at the beginning of the war to work on the Merlin engines at Rolls-Royce. Any small knowledge of lathe work or engineering I have – as opposed to just being a mechanic – must be credited to him. Now as our farming increased it became much more difficult to visit him and eventually, after we decided I must stop, he replaced me with a young student named George Silk. He was signed on as a proper apprentice and very successful he has become. There is now an engineering company in Derby named Silk Engineering and, yes, it has in past years produced an improved version of the Scott motor cycle.

Our Scott underwent a complete overhaul in anticipation of yet another visit to the Isle of Man TT races. We were now a little better off financially so new tyres and chains could be purchased, the engine rebuilt and the whole thing repainted with new Scott transfers fitted on the petrol tank. This tank itself had a story. It was very large (which is why our dogs found it so easy to ride on), completely non-standard, having been specially made for a man competing in the Isle of Man races. It held five gallons of petrol and one of oil. Tom Ward had acquired it on a motor cycle he had bought and being a kind of purist about these things had fitted a standard tank in its place when the bike was sold; so this large tank stood in his store where I saw it. He was put under some pressure to sell it to me but would not do this because he said it would spoil my bike. However, eventually he agreed to toss a coin to see if I should pay him or if I should have it free. The price was to be 1 shilling (or if you prefer it, 5 pence). I lost the toss and had to pay for it but this may have been the best 5 pence I ever spent.

Our holiday was to be financed by another venture into poultry. This time I decided that the day-old cockerel chicks that were being killed in thousands because only laying hens seemed to have a future would be fattened to about twelve weeks old and sold as small chickens – *poussins* was I believe the term being used at that time – so several hundred more fluffy bundles arrived to occupy part of our poultry shed. Since it was possible for me to obtain all the feed needed to raise these chicks from the farm feeds, the profit margin was artificially high and so we had a good piggy bank of holiday money; especially so because the cost of the chicks was only £1 per hundred and I had arranged with a local sawmill to take wood chippings from them at no cost, only haulage – which of course cost me nothing. So we could produce very healthy and clean birds with these nice clean wood chips underfoot. We eventually sold three hundred and had £120 in nice notes in our piggy bank to enjoy our holiday on 'the Island' (as most motor cyclists always call the place).

We stayed at the Wembley hotel on the promenade in Douglas with views over the bay, watched the 'toastrack' horse-drawn trams gently clip-clopping along the centre of the road, stopping here and there to pick up passengers, or caught the electric tram to Laxey up the coast or even to the top of Snaefell mountain. We figured out the workings of the great water wheel at Laxey designed to pump water from the mine there. We journeyed across the fairy bridge and wished the fairies a good day; saw the peacocks at Rushen Abbey and took strawberries and cream there; and above all watched the motor cycle races around the 37¾ mile course specially closed to normal traffic for the day. Taking up one of our favourite positions at Kate's Cottage we would wait for signs of the first rider to appear round the fast left hand bend at around 100 miles per hour, snaking viciously if he was off line by even a few inches and in extreme cases passing within two or three feet of our legs as they dangled over the wall we were sitting on. We were always ready to bale out backwards in an emergency but luckily one never occurred. Sometimes we would take a Primus stove up there to make bacon sandwiches before the race started and believe me no bacon has ever tasted so good. Alas, the do-gooders have now fenced off this part of the

47

course in the name of safety and the races have little appeal to me now: there is no excitement watching distant figures passing, I can do that on the roads near home.

Between race days we rode around the course, the roads being reopened to traffic, but even so it took an hour's hard riding to cover one lap of the course which the riders in the race would cover in about twenty-three minutes, and my respect for the riders increased considerably. After the race it was wonderful to see many of the bikes being taken back to the various garages the riders occupied for the week, not, as you may think, on a trailer or in a van, but ridden by a mechanic through the heart of Douglas with open megaphone exhaust pipes weaving in and out of the traffic with a noise that hurt the ears. It is a great tribute to the horses that drew the trams that they never turned a hair as these noisy bikes passed them. We have since then travelled much further, spent many times the amount of money our 'Island' holidays cost us, but have never exceeded the sheer pleasure that these visits to the TT races gave us.

Shortly after our return from this holiday the Scott motor cycle had trouble with us. (If you think this has been put the wrong way round I will explain.) In the office where Betty worked her colleague, Dorothy, announced that her wedding was imminent and asked Betty to be matron of honour. Betty of course was delighted, always ready for a good party, especially a wedding party, so we became involved in dress organising and fitting and making various other arrangements which feature at weddings. I am no expert at this but was drawn into it as Betty's chauffeur, which culminated in our leaving Dorothy's house after midnight just before the wedding. No, I had not been drinking; at that time (unlike later) I was almost teetotal. A hard day's work

48

before this meant I was very tired, the lane to our village had been newly surfaced, we were in a hurry and the new surface had been turned into a two-wheel-track road with loose chippings in the centre. Travelling at about 55 mph we approached the corner (where, as mentioned in a previous book, I had crashed before) and as I heeled the Scott over and, I guess, being tired did not use the rear brake, just applied the front brake, completely forgetting the loose chippings . . . before I knew it the front wheel locked, the bike went on to full lock and we were on the grass verge. I might have been sleepy at the start but something like this really wakes you up. I came to with a snap, almost saved the situation until the Scott hit a drainage gutter on the grass verge. The front forks bottomed with a crash and the headlamp front flew off. Sudden darkness is a terrible handicap when you are riding a motor cycle and it proved to be on this occasion. The bike stopped faster than any brake could have stopped it by toppling into the ditch, Betty departed at some speed into a field gate (luckily it was open) about twenty-five yards away; I stayed nearer to the bike in the new gravel on the road. There was dead silence, absolute darkness . . . Where was Betty? After a few seconds I shouted 'Where are you?' A voice answered – reassuring, but not much use in the pitch darkness. Eventually we found one another and then found the Scott, but did it take some getting out of the ditch. We replaced the lamp front and rode home, Betty mostly undamaged other than a large black bruise on her forehead, leading to the next day's continual question, 'Whatever have you done to your head?' Without a quiver in her face the answer would be 'He did it', looking at me. I had a sore shoulder – my jacket was torn and ragged with the sleeve almost shredded. We were lucky, I guess.

5

THIS time, the early to mid 1950s, was the most stable of my life, with a reasonable house and a happy marriage. True there were not so many funny or unusual things happening to me as did in the war years but this was, no doubt, partly due to getting older and a little, probably very little, less 'mad' than before. But I was able to learn more skills such as producing balanced feeds for our stock and learning the chemicals best suited to weed control on the farm. We had now purchased a Ransome Cropguard sprayer, using May & Baker 2,4,D weedkiller mostly and the dangerous DNOC on occasion when we found weeds resistant to our usual chemical.

Betty at this time announced that a baby would be arriving, so obviously another skill had been learned. Both sets of parents were overjoyed, and we too were of course extremely pleased. Though we had never planned a baby, equally we had never planned not to have a family. Sadly we lost the baby a few months later, to the deep distress of all the family. This period in our life has never been forgotten but neither of us has carried sadness or bitterness over the ensuing years, believing that it was best to carry on as we had always tried to do and that is what we have done. But Betty was devastated and this feeling took many weeks to recover from.

During the 1950s I was competing in ten or so ploughing matches each year, still using David Brown, but finding it difficult to compete with competitors using trailed ploughs, which were so stable and easier to control. Perhaps I should have used a trailed plough instead of my David Brown mounted plough but this would have meant towing it around on a trailer and also loading and unloading at the various events. Besides, I was convinced that the future of ploughing lay with the mounted plough and did not wish to take what I felt was a retrograde step. I was able to compete to the extent that second and third prizes were readily available but first prize usually eluded me.

With the arrival of Rex another and amusing feature opened up at these matches. Once having acquired the taste for motor cycling he quickly adapted to riding day after day on the tractor. Even when the tractor was not in use he would sit hour after hour on the bench seat in case someone might need the machine and he would be ready to go on a ride, so in this way he started to attend ploughing matches with me. It was very amusing to see people walk up to the tractor standing at the end of my plot only to be greeted with a shining array of white

Rex enjoyed his ploughing matches.

teeth, both lips drawn well back and a throaty snarl bidding spectators to keep clear. They stayed away in a semicircle staring at this cuddly looking black spaniel that had suddenly turned into a savage beast, sometimes twenty or thirty just looking at him whilst I might be making some adjustment or other to the plough. The funny thing was he never got off the tractor and even if he had done so I believe his normally amiable self would have reasserted itself and he would have strolled over to them to be fussed and stroked. Even today, forty years later, a few people still remark about the black dog who used to sit on the tractor seat.

The first winter Rex spent on the farm gave us severe problems. His luxuriant coat, jet black and rather long, with what we described as 'flags' or extra long hair on his legs, plus a long growth of hair on the ears, collected mud like a building site in a thunderstorm and so he quickly became a rather felty-looking object. We tried bathing, which he rather liked; brushing and combing, which he definitely did not like; and finally resorted to scissors. All the felty wogs were cut off and he looked awful; so then we trimmed him all over, which brought a growl and a snap or two but certainly gave an improved appearance. This trying sequence of events, the dewogging of Rex, produced a new name: ever afterwards he was known as Mr Woggins even to the extent of a notice being placed on the back of the tractor seat proclaiming 'Do not touch, Mr Woggins is dangerous'.

Now we had two farms (it could be said we had three if the outlying land at Thulston was counted as one), we found it necessary to reorganise our transport. Betty and I still had the faithful Crossley and the Scott motor cycle, my father had a Rover 16 modified to a kind of pick-up truck for carrying milking equipment to the summer milking fields and he also had the Citroën 12/4 car. This, known in France as the Rosalie, I believe, was the last rear-wheel-drive model I remember being produced by that company. Before the much lower front-wheel-drive model came on the market, the Citroën 12/4 was a really strong motor car, so much so that its performance was affected by its sheer weight. One day I accidentally reversed a trailer into it putting a dent in the front wing, trying to beat it out was very difficult indeed and I found one could hit the wing quite hard with a large hammer and then only get a solid 'dong', quite different from today's silver-paper models. It was a tough old car very suitable for a farmer, carrying bales of hay on the rear seat, the occasional calf to market and always having a few fencing tools in the back, just in case we found a bad piece of fence when inspecting the dairy cows last thing at night during their summer stay in the milking pastures. The engine had a baffle plate in the exhaust manifold which could be turned to give a hot-spot effect for burning low-quality fuel. Someone in the past had fitted a separate fuel tank and a two-way switch, no doubt during the war, so the car could be run on tractor fuel. This it did quite well and cut our motoring costs considerably on long journeys. It was fitted with a freewheel, a device quite popular in the mid to late 1930s, and used a great deal by Rover in this country. It allowed the car to freewheel like a bicycle as an aid to fuel economy. But one did rely on the brakes rather more than on a more normal type of transmission and the brakes on this Citroën were of the dreaded Bendix type which you may remember we had such trials with on the Crossley. However, I used the freewheel a lot but was always most careful when going down hill. The same feature also enabled one to change gear without using the clutch.

Over time the freewheel began to slip and one never quite knew if the car would take off from a standstill smoothly or just wait a split second while the freewheel decided if it would work or not. This meant that starting from a standstill might produce an effect as if someone had hit the bootlid at speed as the Citroën transmission grabbed hold, shooting the car forward. We decided that two cars would have to be replaced by one. The Crossley went first. Bought in 1939 for £7 it was sold in the early fifties for £30. The Citroën was eventually sold for £70 after I had fastened the freewheel up solid and removed the control from the dashboard.

Our local garage had two cars in stock we were interested in, both capable of pulling a cattle trailer. We had decided this was the way to go now the Crossley and the Citroën had departed for pastures new. One of these cars was a Wolseley 21 of 1937 vintage and the other an ex-US Army Chevrolet probably of 1940. The Wolseley had nice black paintwork, wooden dashboard, leather trim and had just gone through a complete engine overhaul, so we chose that one; with hindsight, the wrong one. The Wolseley gave us good service – plenty of power and still doing 22 mpg when driven with care – but it was equipped with two S.U. carburettors, large ones, which poured petrol into the engine like Niagara Falls when all the performance was used.

We still had David Brown, of course. We had often looked at other tractors, realising we should change it, but many things were in favour of keeping it. The only tractor I fancied was an International W4 but this was already an old model and not a diesel. Fordson Major diesels were available but the price seemed just beyond our means, especially so because we still needed more dairy cows, so we just kept on using David Brown. I

54

believe it was the winter of 1954 when we decided to overhaul him completely. Everything I could think of was done and the bill for parts was less than £100. During this period whilst the tractor was stripped I sat looking and thinking about a cab. Most of those on the market were covers not cabs and in my opinion generated noise and draught, so I started a fundamental rebuild of the driver's area. After my experience of rebuilding the Crossley car one might have thought I would have learned something and had more sense, but the Crossley was a long time ago and those difficulties had faded in my memory just a little.

The fuel tank was removed and the cowl or draught deflector around it, still with its shrapnel hole from those wartime adventures. The bench seat and brackets came out too, to be replaced with a car bucket seat, modified to provide adjustment for my comfort. A shaped wooden frame was made extending the full width of the wings, forward to a bulkhead that could now be made just behind the engine because the fuel tank was no longer there; the front bulkhead stopped at bonnet level and a sloping windscreen fitted over it; side panels of aluminium stopped at the same level and vertical side windows carried on to the cab roof level; the roof was curved slightly and made again from aluminium; the space in front of the steering column was taken up with a heater supplied with hot water from the rear of the engine, also a radio was fitted. The fuel tank, removed from a car (guess where it came from), occupied the passenger-seat area as far forward as the front bulkhead and was filled using its original filler, which protruded through a hole in the side panel. Also a toolbox was made in the side panel under the fuel tank.

Looking on this assembly, which had taken nearly two weeks to construct, gave me great pleasure, especially

55

when the hunting-pink paint job was finished. No door was needed on the near side of course but a wide one was made on the driver's side, which could be removed in hot weather. Mr Woggins sat, looking out of the window, on top of the fuel tank and of course the tractor could now only carry one person and not two as it had originally been designed to do. In my innocence the windows were made from ordinary house glass; it never crossed my mind that this might be dangerous if it shattered, but all the years afterwards we never had a broken window.

The weather soon allowed me to try the facelifted tractor on some ploughing. The effect of the changes was almost unbelievable. The gears still had all the David Brown howl and whine but the engine was inaudible from inside the cab; so much so that if one thought the tractor was not running well the door had to be opened so the exhaust note could be heard to establish if all cylinders were firing. Mr Woggins soon stretched out along the fuel tank and fell asleep, so we were both satisfied with our new toy.

We were now mixing all our own dairy rations and so the old open crank engine driving our Bamford mill began to be very temperamental. After all, it had been in service for some years and the demands on it were increasing year by year. Saturday was usually my day for grinding, partly because Father wanted to use the tractor on farm jobs and partly because the contract work we did for other farmers did not call for Saturday working. If Father had not wanted to use the tractor, it would have been possible to cut a hole in the shed wall and drive the mill with David Brown, but in any case I loved the challenge of keeping this kind of Heath Robinson arrangement on the go. It was a constant challenge never to allow the outfit to stop and so I continued my race with water for the engine, fuel, oil, fresh corn and taking off the full bag before the mill had indigestion on over-filled bags of ground corn. I still had not converted the old engine to our expansion-type exhaust system and the pipe still blew outside the shed with an open exhaust. Mother had now moved the rose tree that became the only black rose in England as it progressively got more and more soot on its flowers; it had now reverted to producing its more normal red roses. How the neighbours stood the noise I know not. From experience I knew it was possible to hear the engine and mill quite clearly half a mile away, but they never protested. I guess it is like keeping pigs: if you cannot stand the noise or smell of the country life, just go and enjoy the traffic fumes and Sunday afternoon lawn mowers in the towns.

One day the engine would not start. I turned and turned, but only I got fired up. Red in the face and with an aching back, I sat and looked at the old engine. In truth I was surprised – the old thing was usually the one machine on the farm that would always start. After cleaning the spark plugs for the second time I decided to test for a spark. There was none and cleaning the magneto only showed that the armature insulation had melted. From many adventures with motor cycles I knew this was a terminal situation so . . . no grinding *that* day. My friend Fred was the saviour of the day by producing a Ford Model T coil, so with a rubber band to hold it in place, a piece of brass strip and a six-volt battery plus some small amount of soldering we were ready to see if it worked. We weren't exactly sure where the wonderful spark being produced would occur in relation to the ignition timing. With everything ready Fred looked at me, I looked at Fred, but I guess he could outstare me, so with some trepidation I took up the starting handle. We both knew the strength of the first firing stroke of the old thing. Turning the engine with my thumb over the handle and on the same side as the rest of my hand I yanked it round as violently as possible. It started. Now we could push the coil a little further forward on the mag platform so the brass strip made contact with the magneto cam a little sooner, thus advancing the ignition timing a bit. Ever afterwards we had to remember to slide the coil back a bit before starting the engine or we had the most almighty kick back with flames from the air intake, but it had more power than ever. We ground corn faster but had to carry more water – it now boiled much more violently than before. Only once did I forget to slide the coil back under its rubber band before starting. The result was an extra large thumb which did not work properly for days.

Just imagine what a modern health-and-safety inspector might make of our grinding shed, with its unprotected belt, open tin of petrol, dust, oil-bathed engine and uneven floor. It was used for about fifteen years like that, no one was killed or even injured to any extent but everyone who used it went away a much more careful and aware person. I reckon we did more to make our staff safety conscious than a month of lectures could have achieved.

Just to show how carelessness does have a price I will recount an experience I had one Easter Monday. (I believe the year was 1953, certainly before the cab was in place.) David Brown had a bad attack of the gearbox rumbles so over the Easter holiday it was decided to remove the gearbox to see what had befallen his insides. Having inspected by removing the cover it was decided a bearing failure was at least imminent if not current. The box was removed and a decision taken to remove several bearings and replace them when our local stockist opened after the holiday. One bearing just would not move, so having broken the bearing puller on it I decided that desperate disease called for a desperate remedy: the bearing was warmed with a hot cloth, the shaft laid across our anvil, and a big hammer selected with a view to either breaking the bearing inner race or at least loosening it. (There is a Derbyshire saying, 'Derbyshire born and Derbyshire bred, strong ith'arm and wick ith'yed'; but remember in Derbyshire dialect 'wick' means 'clever'.) So the bearing caught a really heavy blow.

Nothing happened except I felt something in my eye, and looking into the mirror, I could see a sliver of something right in the centre of my eyeball. No one was at home as, it being Easter, everyone had departed for various destinations on holiday. It seemed wrong for me to fiddle with it so I telephoned our doctor. I was on good terms with him because if he was ever in motor-car trouble he would ring me and I was always pleased to attend to it at once. He took one look and said it needed hospital attention, so off I went to the hospital.

The nurse in the casualty department sat me down and sent for the eye doctor. He arrived in his tennis gear, but was very good about it – maybe he had won his match. My shirt was removed, oil and all, I was togged up in a kind of high-necked nightgown and laid on a table in an operating theatre with a white-gowned doctor and two nurses, and a cartwheel-sized mass of lights shining down on me. All most professional, but from here the job went downhill fast. An appliance shaped like a large electric drill but with a pointed end instead of a chuck was produced. It was at this stage I realised that it was an electrical magnet and they were not going to try and drill the sliver out. After I had been clamped down the doctor brought the magnet really close to my eye.

Nothing happened. He pulled the trigger several times, then decided it was not switched on! The nurse traced the cable from the operating table to the wall and reported there was no plug on the cable end. A quick check with the hospital administration office disclosed that no electrician would be on duty before the evening, and as neither nurse nor doctor had been trained to fix a plug, the job was stopped.

Derbyshire born and Derbyshire bred, strong ith'arm, wick ith'yed, but no electric?

'Unstrap me,' I said, 'and I will do it.' We found a surgical instrument that seemed as if it could be used as a screwdriver and took a plug from a tool looking very much like a saw (I wondered how many bones that had cut through). With the plug in place and the magnet nicely buzzing I was strapped down again.

Now the magnet tried hard. It buzzed as it came ever closer to my eye; the nurses peered from the side; the

60

doctor braced himself against the table and came even closer – but to no avail. It was decided that the magnet was just not strong enough. The doctor decided that we would try the other theatre, so after I had been un-strapped once again a troop of white-clad figures trailed off down the passage. This theatre had an immense mag-net fully five feet tall with a pointed piece sticking out at the top. The doctor showed the nurse the correct pedal to press to obtain full power and after telling me what he intended to do held my head in a vice-like grip and pushed my eye towards the magnet. 'NOW!' he said to the nurse. The magnet hummed and a sliver of steel was stuck to the point of the magnet. My eye was washed out, a wad of cotton wool held with sticking plaster put over it and I was sent home after being told to report back next day at 9 am.

I found how different a hospital is on a normal day as opposed to a bank holiday. The world and his wife seemed to be there – and most of his children. I checked in and was sat down on one of the lines of forms already almost full of humanity. After an hour and a half of waiting I decided that was enough and wished I had pulled the sliver out with tweezers in the first place, I took off the cotton wool and went home to get on with some work.

Now common sense took over and I took the shaft to an engineering friend of mine who removed the damaged bearing, so after collecting the required new bearings David Brown could be put together again. The removal of the bearing and consequent rebuilding of the shaft cost £1. What a lot of trouble for so little cost! David Brown ran beautifully quiet and looked set to stay with us for some time yet.

6

ABOUT this time we lost Mr Woggins. The engine and mill had been grinding oats all day, Mr Woggins sniffing and snuffling around the pile of oat sacks at the rear of the shed and generally wandering around the farmyard, no doubt collecting another set of muddy wogs for us to cut off at some future date when we got around to giving him a spring clean. The fact that he disappeared was not unusual. My mother, who still came on Saturday to look at the battery hens and collect eggs, often took him with her. She felt it amusing to let him carry an egg into the house for her, his soft spaniel mouth never breaking the shell. However, it was vital to arrive in the house before him so one could take the egg from his mouth or he would take it to the egg table and just open his mouth and let it go with a disastrous splash on to the floor. After tea Betty asked where Mr Woggins was, and immediately a 'dog hunt' started, all around the farm, the sheds, the village, the nearby fields until dark. It was a depressed household that night. We decided perhaps he had wandered down the road and climbed into someone's car. Then we thought of his love for water. The nearest water was what we called the sludge dyke that carried the drains away from the village down to the river. It had steep sides and quite probably he would not be able to climb them if he had decided to go for a swim. The quality of the water never worried him; he would swim in soup if necessary and sludge dyke was just about the consistency of soup but with funny yellowish green colours running through it. The water – if that is what it could be called – was stagnant now since the village had its new sewage system installed with its pump and shredder for solids, so the liquid could be pushed two or so miles to the sewage farm. We knew he would not be particular about water quality because in the past he had decided to cool off in the thick brown soup that surrounded the farm muck heap. (Perhaps it had a particular quality not apparent to us.) We had to hose him down after these excursions. In the darkness we decided to take a lamp and make sure he was not stuck in the sludge dyke; but there was no Mr Woggins and we had to return home depressed and unhappy.

The next morning we searched again, calling him. He responded to his name quite well now so any stranger in our village may have regarded us as 'lock-up' cases as we trailed around calling 'Mr Woggins'. Just before midday, as was normal on Sunday, my father and grandfather came to visit. Grandad looked around the garden adjoining the grinding shed and called us to listen. There was a rather pathetic whining noise . . . He had found Mr Woggins. We assume he had been mousing amongst the oat bags which were stacked three high and had either chased a mouse or just fallen between the sacks; anyway there he was stuck vertically face down. Obviously his reverse gear was not up to the job of extricating him. I suppose he must have spent about eighteen hours stuck in this uncomfortable place, we soon had him out and apart from being stiff he seemed little the worse for his experience. This must have been the most futile adventure of his life – even if he caught a mouse he could never kill it, just carry it around until it drowned in his mouth.

My father had been using the Rover 16 truck for carrying the milking equipment for some time and it had begun to prove unreliable, and since it also needed a set of tyres we decided to replace it with another tractor. Having seen a David Brown advertised in a farm sale we attended the event intending to purchase if possible. It turned out to be a very early model, possibly of 1940 manufacture; it even had the original cast-iron radiator grille quite undamaged. The machine looked as if it had not done too much work and the engine ran quite well. It eventually made £120 and we now had two David Brown tractors – but how to get the new one home? We could have driven it but there was no licence on it and we did not have insurance to cover it so we decided to tow it with the Wolseley car. (We always carried a tow rope; indeed I still do.) The tractor was hitched behind the car and, giving my father strict instructions to go slow, I took my place on the tractor. Now the Wolseley was a big car and very quiet, so 30 mph was very slow for the car but very fast if you sat on a tractor hitched behind it on a seat with flat springs and exposed to the wind. I was soon bobbing about like a tin can on a string, my eyes watering as I tried to keep the tractor from straying outside the dimensions of the car. This was very difficult to do but not as difficult as trying to stop. As we came to the first downhill section I began to catch up with the car. At this stage the tractor brakes began to show a complete indifference to working. I had my back against the rear of the seat, foot pushing the brake pedal so hard it was almost bending, both hands pulling desperately on the two steering brake handles in an attempt to increase pressure on the footbrake system, and also trying to steer with my spare knee. Eventually I caught up with the car but was able to direct one front wheel onto the tow bar. This directed my father's attention to focus sharply on the situation. We were able to stop safely and I engaged a gear on the tractor so on the next downhill section I was able to release the clutch and thus gently slow down with some engine braking. The journey was about 25 miles, so at the end my left leg had a will of its own for a few hours.

Our new tractor proved very successful. The milking equipment was carried on a low trailer and so my father did not have to lift heavy churns etc. as high as with the Rover, saving him a great deal of heavy work. He was just beginning to suffer hip problems which eventually would put a stop to our farming activities. All through his life he had been carrying heavy weights; even in the 1920s when he was employed as a wagoner at Locking-ton it was a tradition that the wagoner carried corn from the threshing machine and in those days the normal size of sack was 18 stones or 252 lb and often had to be carried up steps to a first-floor granary. Two or three days of that work must have been a killer. Even when he drove the lorry in later years it was not unusual for the farmer to expect deliveries to be made up steps to his granary. Worst of all were the bags of beans. These were 19 stones (266 lb). Little wonder that the ordinary cattle-food bag of 1 cwt seemed like a feather to him. Even when doing the milking at home in the winter he was always carrying bales of hay or straw and of course the milking machine units up the yard from the cowshed and then up three steps to the dairy – so little wonder his joints were getting worn.

Because we were mainly a dairy farm it was necessary to make as much hay as possible and later silage, even buying growing grass from other farmers when possible. The cost of baling seemed to be rising steeply so we decided to purchase our own baler. The contractor who had baled our hay up to this time used an International B45 model and this decided us to try and find one the same. We telephoned the local dealer who usually had a stock of used machines. The B45 at this time was a best-seller. Calling at the depot to inspect the baler we found the sales staff were all out but the service manager, Ben Mowson, took us to the used-machinery lot and showed us what was available. He recommended one baler in particular, rather rusty but (as he said and I could see) in good order. He apologised that it had not been repainted as it normally would have been but pressure of work meant that it would be three weeks before it could be done, we could take it at a reduced price as it was if we wanted to start right away; they would deliver it and send a fitter to start us off. So we had a baler and I had met Ben Mowson for the first but not the last time.

The baler was installed and the sales representative called round to collect the money for it. Again I met a man, Allan Beaumont, who would be part of my life later. Our baler brought us peace of mind during the hay season, knowing we could bale at just the right time; also, and perhaps just as important, we could undertake a great deal of work for neighbouring farmers. This earned us a considerable amount of money and along with the crop-spraying and milk production meant we were getting much more prosperous. This inevitably made the tax man come sniffing around, and for the first time we were having to pay an accountant to present our accounts in an understandable manner. To me this time was the beginning of the tax system starting to dampen initiative and lead to the depression and unemployment we have today. Politics barely enter into this; whichever party is in power a strict tax system seems to allow the very few best business people to accumulate money at an enormous rate which the less cute small companies cannot match; and so they gradually decline, with consequent unemployment and misery. The more unemployment we get the more money we have to find and those in work must pay higher taxes to meet the bills. At some stage I guess all will give up work or, if they are rich enough, just emigrate to another country where good management and efficiency are appreciated and not blighted by overblown taxes. Of course, we have trade unions who one may reasonably think would help protect their workers, but the unions seem to me only interested in confrontation with management to cure all ills. Maybe later experiences have coloured my judgement but I have not seen any progress made to spread the wealth of our nation even reasonably fairly over a period of forty or so years.

During the mid 1950s there was a particularly bad harvest in our Trent Valley area. It rained and rained. With a great effort we managed to cut our harvest with the Albion Yeoman binder and stook up the sheaves, where it stood through weeks of rain until we perceived a few corns beginning to grow in the stook. It was far too wet to cart and stack so we decided it must be threshed in the field. A combine harvester seemed the right way to go but all combine owners were struggling with their own harvest. In desperation we looked around for a combine harvester we could buy and eventually found a Grain Marshall at a farm in Ruddington near Nottingham, we purchased it for £100 and were told it had only been used for one harvest and then left unused because it was too slow. I think it was a four foot six inch cut but I am not sure about this; anyway it seemed just what we required.

Our Grain Marshall was powered by a Ford 1172cc engine, a typically heavy British machine, petrol fired and without a vestige of paint. Presumably it had been painted silver when new but that finish had long since fallen off. I later spent a week restoring the silver and the thing then looked quite smart. With the combine in our yard we could not wait to start our harvesting operation but there was a snag: the engine had caught 'Forditis' and would not start. A new battery was provided, plugs, points and the carburettor breathed on with bated breath but still it would not run. I even tried the old trick of putting a lighted match down the plughole, that had set the model F tractor on fire all those years ago, but to no avail. We filled it with boiling water and heated the manifold with a blowlamp and it fired but would not run. I now assumed the valves were rusty and not seating correctly, or were stuck, so I lubricated the guides and left it until next morning, when we found a belt long enough to turn it with David Brown. We ran it for about an hour, took off the belt and pulled the starter and off it went. It proved to be a wonderful engine after this first problem, using no oil and always starting easily. The experience just added to my conviction that 'Forditis' is all to do with valves and thus easy to cure.

We took our ungainly machine down the main A6 road with the usual dire results for the drivers who always felt they had urgent business to attend to (or perhaps a mistress waiting in some quiet den), and then began our threshing. The idea was very good; the grain was awful, wet, green and growing. We managed to find enough sacks to hold all this wet grain and they stood with open tops in our hay barn gently steaming and most likely going mouldy as well. The local grain-driers could not accept any more grain for several weeks so it looked as if our stock feed for this winter would be of sub-standard quality. At this stage I had a brainwave: strips of old sacks were cut and wrapped around a brush handle then pushed into a sack of wet grain and the handle withdrawn, leaving a sacking chimney to ventilate the grain. Twenty sacks were done with three chimneys in each sack. Next morning the amount of steam coming from those chimneys was unbelievable. It took us two days to prepare all the other sacks but we were drying grain. We found an old winnowing machine in a farm sale, bought it and fixed it up in the Romney hut. As the sacks dried we put the grain through the machine to clean all the rubbish and green bits out and our winter feed problem seemed to improve. With all this work being foisted upon us, do you wonder that my ambitions to be a farmer declined with every sack of grain we handled?

My father's hips were playing him up rather badly and I had to become involved much more in the milking operation. This I could do quite well – but how I hated it! Cows really are awful creatures to be involved with. When I was required to work on other farms doing contract work, and especially when I could get some demonstrations to do for a local dealer, it was bliss. About this time International Harvester introduced a new tractor, the B250, and I could see where our next tractor might come from. David Brown was still going strong but getting more outdated as time went on. However, seeing Allan Beaumont one day sparked me off to suggest I compete with the new tractor at the ploughing matches and afterwards use it on a demonstration plot. He suggested I put this to the sales manager, Mr (Bob) Martin; so I contacted Messrs Cripps of Nottingham and spoke to him. A few days later Allan came back to say he was in agreement but only if I stopped doing demonstrations for other dealers; in addition I must use an IH plough in all the competitions. This seemed OK to me, especially as they asked me to do some demonstrations for them if needed. I considered this to be a wonderful opportunity and a new B250 arrived for me to accustom myself to before the ploughing matches came along.

Now my ploughing match awards became easier to obtain and also I won more first prizes, leading me to compete in the British Ploughing Match at Ratho near Edinburgh and the next year at Tilton on the Hill near Grantham. Meanwhile as the ploughing matches finished my beloved B250 had to return to its owners and I was left again to work with David Brown. I kept him mechanically good so the work output did not deteriorate too much in spite of his venerable age. According to my crude log books there were close on 15,000 hours' work behind him now, but we were making more and more demands upon him in the 1950s; we had begun to grow sugar beet, partly because it was a cash crop and partly due to the return crop of dried and wet beet pulp we were entitled to purchase to help out our home mixed food rations for the stock. Usually we grew six or seven acres – not much, you might say, but with one man occupied almost full time with the cows, and myself contracting out for other farmers, and our only other member of staff working shifts at the local power station, we struggled to keep ahead of the growth. No sugar beet harvesters or mechanical thinners in those days, at least not for us; we worked the crop by hand until the tractor ploughed them out and we followed pulling each loosened beet, knocking the soil from the roots and laying them in rows ready to go again down the row a day or so later to cut off the tops from which the sugar was supposed to have now 'sweened' back into the root. We left alternate piles of roots and tops ready to collect with the tractor and trailer, beet to the factory and tops to feed the dairy cows (usually pushing the milk yield up a gallon or two). The roots were carted to the roadside ready for a lorry to collect and carry to the factory at Colwick near Nottingham. The cash from this crop was a welcome addition to our income, but knocking beet or cutting tops on a frosty October morning with frozen hands which quickly became wet and painful left little to be pleased about. Even the contemplation of a smaller overdraft on the bank statement seemed somehow a poor reward for this pain; even the hoeing and singling of the crop seemed always to be done in clammy mist, downpours of rain or burning sun.

After one year I decided the whole job must change. (I told you hard work was against my religion.) For the next year's crop I found a Garner two-wheel tractor with plough and cultivator, 600cc Norton engine, three-speed and reverse gearbox, which seemed just what was wanted. With its centrifugal clutch it seemed an ideal hoeing tractor. Now Grandad Hardy had a large garden. He was close to eighty years old so I volunteered to plough his garden with my new toy. The fact that the centrifugal clutch tended to stick had not yet penetrated my brain – it always worked well when run around the farmyard. In my wisdom I decided to plough the garden one way so it would remain level, leaving only two small headlands to dig when the tractor had finished. All went well, with the Norton engine pulling like a train at low revs, and after a few runs the soil looked quite good. I got more confident with the tractor and opened up the throttle a little more, partly to break up the soil as it was turned and partly to speed up the return journey in reverse gear when not ploughing. Shutting the throttle at the end of a reverse run I expected the tractor to stop. I was disappointed: the tractor just kept going. The engine at tick over had plenty of power to keep the machine on the move and before I knew what was happening the two

71

handles were into the hedge with me, trapped between them, being pushed backwards through a strong thorn hedge. It felt like being attacked by 'Jaws'. Luckily my shoulders and head were above the hedge, but oh my legs, thighs and bottom were scratched and gouged, full of thorns. It was several days before I felt like a good sit down and even longer before all the thorns were removed. As Betty said, it was a good thing I was pushed backwards and not forwards through the hedge.

The tractor proved quite a success at hoeing sugar beet which we drilled with our Sunshine corn drill, blocking off the drills we did not want to use and thus getting our rows 21 inches apart. The Garner was arranged with discs and hoe feet and thus was able to hoe very close to the plants, leaving only a few inches to finish by hand when singling. I spent hours in that field going up and down, the centrifugal clutch proving a boon because it made it possible to control the tractor with the twist grip throttle with one hand and steer the hoe with the other.

The singling of our beet was done by an Irish chap who happened to call one day looking for work, so his labour saved us from that chore. We treated him well and he agreed to come back in the autumn and harvest the crop. The haulage costs of taking the crop to Nottingham were fairly steep, so during the summer whilst the beet was growing I looked around for a good trailer. I found one as part of Charlie's equipment (Charlie of course being the first farmer I worked for and had the adventures with the Fordson model F). He had by now moved to a larger farm and was also growing beet. We soon reached an agreement where I would haul the beet from both farms using his trailer and our tractor so it seemed our haulage costs would be cut substantially. Mick our Irishman, a very good worker, we hoped would return and harvest both crops. He eventually telephoned us setting a date to begin, so our second sugar beet harvest was much easier than the first and, I hoped, more profitable.

The journey to the beet factory at Colwick on the outskirts of Nottingham was about fifteen miles. Unfortunately the factory was just on the other side of the city so we had either to cross the centre each time or make a much longer trip around it. I was quite used to this journey because when we had the haulage business I would be drafted in to do the odd trip. Charlie's trailer carried 4 tons of beet and weighed about 1 ton and David Brown even with water-ballasted rear wheels only just topped $1\frac{1}{2}$ tons, so care needed to be taken on down gradients and long sight was required to avoid panic stops at traffic lights. Our first loads went off quite well, the weather being kind, and our target of one load each day was easily attainable. With Mick to help load and the pressure wash at the beet factory to blast off the beet I began to enjoy our beet crop. Mr Woggins also was much in favour, as he could spend day after day in his beloved tractor cab. Unfortunately his day would be marred by the water jet which hammered into the trailer bottom with a loud thundering noise, splashing water around and spotting up the cab windows. He attacked each splash with bared teeth, never catching one of course but never giving up trying. Each load had to be delivered to the factory under a permit system. If you arrived without a permit to unload, often you would be sent away to return another day. This led to a kind of black market in permits and a few eggs would usually ensure extra permits being made available, allowing us to take loads straight from the field and thus avoid the extra work in carting the beet to the roadside and reloading it when a permit was available. Extra permits suited me because it was possible to keep finding extra days to do contract work or ploughing matches, as well as preparing our winter-wheat ground; so the sooner the beet haulage was finished the better. It also meant we were paid sooner.

Of course our journeys were not without incident. With plenty of permits available I decided on two loads each day. With no lights on the trailer we could not start before 7 am and the return had to be made before 11 am so that the second load could be completed by 5 pm. All was well until an early frost covered the road. Our journey meant we had to cross a Bailey bridge erected by army engineers to serve as a temporary replacement for Cavendish bridge in Shardlow. It was approached by a short sharp incline, the single line traffic being controlled by traffic lights. This particular morning I was stopped just at the foot of the incline. When the lights changed to green David Brown started off a few yards and then hit the incline; at that stage we only made forward progress as the slipping tyres melted the frost off the road surface. However, we eventually arrived on the bridge just in time to meet the traffic from the other direction which by this time had received its green signal. The result was chaos – hooters blowing, drivers shouting . . . As on other occasions when I took to the road with a tractor and hit problems, it was the time of day when many people were trying to arrive at work on time. After ten minutes of this, things began to improve. Mr Woggins did his best by trying to attack everyone who walked past. Looking back now I can smile at this incident and cannot help wondering what a local radio station might have made of this situation, had there been such a thing as local radio at that time. It might have sounded like this: 'Here is the road report. The A6 at Shardlow is blocked by some idiot and a peculiar black dog trying to cross the Bailey bridge on a red tractor pulling a heavy load . . .' Ever afterwards I held back from the traffic light so a good fast run could be made at the gradient up to the bridge. Of course we had to travel through the centre of Nottingham at around 8.30 am, which added more dismay and consternation to the journeys, but I always took the view that he who worries is lost.

Another mishap occurred when one day I forgot to fill up with fuel for the second trip. The fuel ran out as I entered Nottingham on the return journey. With very little petrol in the tank and no filling station around I spied a hardware shop with a sign proclaiming it sold Esso Blue paraffin. Scraping around for change I found enough to buy two gallons, so off we went again. The ignition knock and pinking had to be heard to be believed; running as rough as the proverbial hairy bear we eventually arrived home.

7

ONE of the things about the 1950s which will always remain in my mind is the number of vagrants or tramps travelling up and down the A6 road, usually scruffy individuals supposedly looking for work but, if offered it announcing that they had a job lined up but were having to walk because they had not the money for the fare. Those years seemed to me to be much worse than the so-called depression years of the 1990s. It could be quite frightening to arrive at our summer milking shed around 6.30 am to find a rough and scruffy individual who had just been woken up by the arrival of the tractor. All these travellers had only to go about half a mile further and could have stayed overnight in a clean bed with a meal thrown in, all for free at the workhouse or 'spike' as we called it; but of course they did not use these facilities because they were expected to work in the gardens until midday and work was something most of them did not understand.

We used to collect ashes from the Shardlow spike to mend our roads and gateways. I remember these bad old times because in another part of the spike was a building housing the hospital for those unfortunates who were homeless or deranged and could not survive in an open society. Such individuals were treated very badly by some members of the staff, but in the main well fed and cared for. On one occasion we arrived to collect ashes and were allocated two men to help load our trailer. These two were quite sensible and, despite speech difficulties, eventually managed to convey to us a request for a cigarette. I had none but promised to bring some on the next load, in fact I promised a packet each day if they worked well. Ashes flew on that trailer; I could imagine the shovels might be hot at the end of loading. How they worked and how strong they were! I could well see the problems the staff might have with such strong fellows if they were crossed. How they controlled them I do not know but they must have had some way I knew nothing about, as these patients were obviously terrified of the staff.

Despite such reminders that life has its darker side, for me, entering my thirties, the 1950s were a good decade. It is impossible for me to say anything but good of them. Perhaps for Betty and my mother the loss of our baby cast more of a shadow than it did for me, but we were living well and having good holidays, hoping of course that our looked-for family would arrive in due course.

We were still getting floods in our village and some-times into the house, usually when heavy rain coincided with a thaw of the snow sitting on the hills in the Peak of Derbyshire where our river, the Derwent, originated. The village had a flood defence system but in one place an old road crossed the embankment, consequently the constant traffic of tractors and animals had worn this down quite a piece. With the river rising quite fast and rain still falling we received a flood warning from the river board. One of the farmers who used this road decided it had better be repaired at once, or the water would be in the village sooner than it really should be. All he could think of to use as repair material to stop up this low place was a few loads of cow manure tipped into the gap and levelled up to the height of the flood bank, so this solid muck bound with urine-soaked straw was soon dumped into the breach and all seemed well. But this was to be a big flood and although we did not know it at first we soon found out as the waters continued to rise. I knew they were rising fast because about every hour I walked down our field to inspect a brick I had placed at the edge of the water; often an hour or so later it would be covered as the water neared the top of the flood bank. Residents who had seen all this before lifted their furniture up on to piles of breeze blocks or oil drums, emptied the lower cupboards, took up rugs or mats from the floors, and retired upstairs, with a Primus stove and some fuel in case the electric went off; then just waited.

The first signs of trouble arriving were the street drains starting to overflow. Remember the sludge dyke where we looked for Mr Woggins when he went missing? Well, this festering dyke was filled by the river and started to flow backwards with its evil smell through the drains and into the street. It did little harm other than make a mess, because if the river really broke loose it washed it all away. That is not to say the river was clean, but in your lounge it used to leave only silt and the odd dead fish, which could be washed away with a hosepipe and brush, whereas it took months for the floors and walls to dry. This year was different. I checked the brick marker about 11.30 pm and it had almost disappeared. The water was nearing the top of the flood bank; the roar of crude strength from the river was quite frightening when one was standing in darkness just thirty or so yards from it. I shone my high-power torch across towards the watercourse and could see debris and bits of tree rushing past faster than a man could run; so, deciding another flood was inevitable, I took the car down the lane to slightly higher ground so at least we stood some chance of fetching food, then decided to go to bed. As we lay there we could both hear the distant roar of the river but we eventually slept, to be awakened by the lapping of water. It was light and we could see from our bedroom window the water flowing past down the street. Unfortunately the unusually high flood had broken the farmer's dam of cow manure and the flow down the street carried not only the remains of his structure but a strong smell of cows whilst we all shared his watery green muck and had a high watermark stain of a greeny brown colour around our house walls. He was not a popular man in Ambaston that year.

As I have mentioned, R. Cripps and Co. supported my ploughing match ventures with the loan of a B250 tractor and plough that year. They had been supporting a young farmer for a few years previous to this, so Bill Yates and I travelled around as a team, Allan Beaumont acting as team manager, and between us we provided a good publicity back-up for the company. Usually one of us would win in our class whilst the other would figure in the awards somewhere. As well as always showing the tractor and plough off to its best ability there was the necessity of figuring in the list of awards in the local farming press, to keep both the equipment and the company's name in print so the farmers could read it as they sat by the fire in the evenings. The pressure of this continuous need to do well was quite new to me and would stand me in good stead in future years. The pressure built up especially when the ground did not suit the I.H.Ace plough bodies we were using and we were being subjected to scrutiny by the sales manager, or the local rep whose area we happened to be ploughing in turned up with guarded remarks like, 'I think that plough should work better than that.' Luckily we were usually doing quite well; nevertheless I much appreciated the support that enabled me to win enough prize money to compete in the 1957 British Ploughing Match at Ratho near Edinburgh. This was the highlight of my ploughing year. Allan Beaumont and his wife Beryl plus three spaniels and Betty and I plus Mr Woggins all made the trip to our accommodation in a mobile home in Ratho, quite near the competition site. Messrs Cripps transported the plough and International Harvester provided a new B250 tractor for my use.

My father and our farm helper Ernie held the fort whilst we were away, although my father's hips were gradually getting more painful. We lost no time in taking our dogs for a long walk to work off some of the surplus energy built up during the long journey north, a walk which encompassed a visit to the nearest butcher to purchase a quantity of good Scotch steaks, thus setting our standard of food for the whole of our stay. This was not the first time Betty and I had been to Scotland, in fact we had travelled right around the top of that country up to John o'Groats and across to Cape Wrath along the main trunk road A836, which at that time was single track in many places and had grass growing up the middle. Allan and Beryl had not been to Scotland before so we were again able to enjoy with them the magnificent sight of the Forth Bridge and hear the roar of the trains as they cross it, looking for all the world like Hornby models, so much are they dwarfed by the bridge. (And of course no Forth Road Bridge at that time, although its location was already projected.)

Back to the ploughing and all the people I was destined to meet for the first time here and again so many times in the future: Alfred Hall the secretary of the British Ploughing Association, Mike Bowen of International Harvester, George Wood from the local dealer and later also of International Harvester.

With the new tractor collected from the I.H. compound and mated up with my plough it was time to do some practising for the event. I am not a great believer in practising; if you have your own tractor and plough I am convinced a sight of ground conditions should mean you are capable of using equipment you know and getting the best from it, but on this occasion it was felt better to be sure a new and unused tractor was working as we would wish. When competing in a match I am a firm believer in concentrating on one's own plot to the exclusion of all others.

In this ploughing match I believe the occasion may have got to me a bit and affected my performance, but even so, a placing in the lower twenties was not too bad in a large class. Anyway we had a wonderful time with our friends and shall always remember this time shared with two good people; and although we are not now in close contact this is due in most part to the nomadic type of life I was soon to lead, which affected not only this relationship but that existing with many of our relations and friends.

Back home the routine of ploughing, delivering sugar beet to Colwick, helping my father more and taking a bigger share in the general farm duties went on. My father wanted me to take more responsibility for the dairy side of the farm but this was not in my nature and although he tried many and varied arguments I resisted them all, and with hindsight I still feel I was right to do so. Both my parents were concerned for my wellbeing in the future, believing that in this competitive world my lack of a formal education would not allow me to thrive without the involvement of the whole family. But eventually it was agreed that if I could find suitable employment elsewhere my father, now approaching sixty years of age, would retire. The answer proved to be R. Cripps and Co., who offered me a chance to become a member of their agricultural team (in fact as a fitter with a responsibility to do the demonstration work) and still compete in ploughing matches. I had already qualified for a place in the 1958 British match, which was to be held in their territory, so this deal was just what I needed; besides the wages were nearly double what I had been taking from the farm in weekly income, but of course there would be less freedom and no perks such as use of a car. And so with no family, and Betty working full time, we considered we would be in a good position to continue to lead our happy and fulfilled life.

The early months of 1958 were a hectic time. Our farm sale was fixed for early March, so even more and better rations were needed to make sure the stock were in tiptop shape for the sale, and in these last weeks our mill and the old engine worked harder than ever. So did I. Cripps wanted me to start work in January so I would have a few months' experience before the harvest season, during which the service manager (my new boss Ben Mowson) and his team of mobile fitters were particularly under pressure owing to the high volume of baler sales, demonstrations, and of course the start-up of new machines. This meant grinding and mixing animal rations at weekends or under artificial lights in the week so that we could enjoy at least a little of our former social life. We really needed to make the farm sale successful; my father and mother needed all possible financial back-up to make their retirement thoroughly comfortable. Betty and I had another problem: where should we live when the farm at Thulston was no longer my parents' home? Obviously they would return to Ambaston to live in that house which would revert to a cottage whilst the land was destined to be farmed by a neighbour.

Before we pass on to a new chapter in my life I believe a few words should be written about Grandad Hardy, who died during the 1950s – the one thing marring a fantastic ten years for me. No one knew how old he was; no record of his birth was ever found, but a sister estimated that in 1930 he was sixty-five years old. Eventually he was allowed to claim his old age pension. He had what he called his 'box', an obviously home-made chest of extremely hard, well-varnished oak with 'John Hardy 1875' carved neatly on the lid. I feel sure this would be the year he left home to enter service on a farm, probably at the age of twelve years. After his death I kept this chest until the movements of houses after my father's retirement meant it was left at Ambaston and probably later thrown away – a great pity. He met Granny about the turn of the century and was always proud to recall that during the celebrations for the new century held in the grounds of Elvaston Castle he was the only man who could climb the greasy pole and by doing so won a pig. This animal became part of their family, it gave them many piglets and eventually became so large that if, as was its habit, it came into the house, the table was likely to move around on its back.

At the beginning of this new century as cycling was getting popular, Grandad built himself a bicycle out of parts bought in week by week as he could afford them. It took three months to complete this machine and he rode it until he was in his eighties just before his death. It was an unusual machine and I do not know what became of it. I only wish I had it now. Probably Granny gave it to a scrap man when she moved to the next village. Grandad never mounted the cycle in the normal way but had a long extension to the rear axle upon which he placed his foot, pushed off with his other foot and swung up and over the seat to start pedalling. Later in life he had great difficulty keeping straight and was always asking me to tighten the bearings in the front forks to help him hold his line. In fact he had probably always had this problem but in former times with little or no traffic on the road it would not be noticed; in contrast as the years advanced and motor vehicles became more frequent and faster I have no doubt it became very noticeable, probably even frightening. We were all worried about his wellbeing but with stubborn indifference he just kept on riding. The bicycle had only one brake, on the rear wheel. The other lever on the handlebar worked a small wheel on the front forks; when the lever was pulled this wheel contacted the front tyre and in rotating activated another lever which struck a bell mounted just above it. A very unusual system – I never knew if it was his own invention or a normal device in use during the early years of this century.

Luckily I do have one of his prize possessions still left with me, a rocking chair made, so he told me, by a blacksmith to enable his master, who suffered from 'screws' (I thought this disease was probably arthritis), to rise more easily. His only other prize possession was an old, well-polished organ with a mirror at its back and a brass candlestick each side. How a relatively uneducated countryman came to possess this musical instrument I know not, but he did and could also play it, though only hymn tunes. These he would also sing when chopping kindling wood or logs in his shed – always hymns. As he never attended church I was always intrigued to know why, but never found out.

He never stayed in bed after 5.30 am and usually retired at 9 pm. He would sit in his chair with a good fire, winter or summer, and as 9 pm approached he would announce imperiously 'I will have my sop', this being a basin of tea with broken bread in it which was always his last meal of the day. This constant use of the open fire burning a good deal of wood created quantities of soot in the chimney so the chimney sweep was a regular visitor but as time went on the need for the sweep to visit became more and more frequent. 'It wants the pot scraping,' Grandad would announce. 'I will do it when there is a nice day.' As he was now around eighty years old the thought of his climbing up to the top of his chimney gave us all the collywobbles; nevertheless I came home one day to find he had borrowed a ladder and was preparing to 'do the chimney'. He had the ladder up to the end of the house, a rope around his shoulder, scraper in his pocket, and half a brick. He never had any fear of heights and up he went. Standing astride the ridge of the roof he scraped the chimneypot. Apparently there remained only a small aperture in it, the rest having been blocked with pure carbon, which he soon had scraped clean. The brick was tied to the rope and lowered down the chimney. At the bottom Granny tied on a set of holly branches specially cut for the job; these he hauled up the chimney, and then threw down for another go. Thus their chimney was swept.

One day when Betty cycled home from the office where she worked for midday dinner cooked by Granny, she came running across to me (I happened to be working at home that day). 'Granny says will you come quickly – Grandad is acting queer.' I found him sitting in his rocking chair by the fire as usual, but this time absolutely naked. 'Whatever are you doing like that?' I asked. His reply was: 'The Lord sent me here naked and he will take me away the same.' 'Well, I think you are embarrassing the ladies,' I said, 'and you should let me help you upstairs.' Alas, he could not stand, so I carried him up the stairs and laid him on his bed where he died some hours later in the little house that had seen so much of his life, the hard work, the happy times when the family came for their summer holidays, his contented retirement.

We had lost a good friend and one of the real characters of this century. We reckoned he was well towards his ninetieth year, but no one really knew.

8

WITH my new job occupying my time and spending as many hours as possible helping to prepare for the farm sale, I found the beginning of 1958 a very hectic but very enjoyable time. After a few weeks at work and visiting farms with another fitter doing winter services on balers and combines I was allocated a van, so at last became mobile in my own right. My van was a Commer which had been used by the industrial side of the I.H. dealership and thus was now handed down to the poorer agricultural side. Ben Mowson, our agricultural service manager, soon had it equipped with the many spares one needed to carry around both for balers and combines whilst I obtained a few pieces for use when demonstrating tractors. All these spares were checked by me and signed for, many hundreds of pounds' worth of new spares beautifully stored in drawers and cabinets built into the van by the bodybuilding section of the company. I had to supply my own tool kit, but this was no problem as I had plenty. At this time such things as socket sets and spanners were quite cheap. Most of mine, usually of American manufacture, came from ex-Ministry of Defence sales, and I still have many of them today as good as ever; they probably cost me no more than £5 the lot.

Betty and I were now under pressure to find ourselves a house. I had hoped to find a farm cottage and I became lucky. While dropping some spares off at a farm in Lockington where I had lived some thirty years before, I asked the son of the farm, Willy Thomson, if anything was available. He suggested I look at a spare cottage which was part of their second farm, where he and his wife Hazel and daughter Kim lived, whilst his father had the main farm in the village. Soon after Betty and I looked at the cottage, just big enough for us and adjoining a second cottage where the farm worker lived. It was about a mile up a narrow lane and really remote. There were no drains and no mains water; we were back to a bucket-type toilet, or 'petty', down the garden and water which had to be carried from a well shared by both families. So gone were the nice flush toilet and bathroom we had become accustomed to after the modernisation at Ambaston; now if you wanted to visit the toilet on a cold night it was a case of putting on a top coat and carrying a flashlight, whilst water heated in an electric boiler (yes, we had electric) had to be carried to the tin bath in front of the fire and, worse, had to be carried out again after we were nice and clean and warm. To those not used to taking a bath in front of the fire let me say there are compensations for all the work involved. It is nice and warm, and even romantic to have your back scrubbed by your spouse; but do not put the bath too near the fire – it can overheat your ambitions and, as I know by experience, cause a severe burn if you lean your leg on the side of a tin bath pre-heated by a raging fire.

My father allowed me to inherit David Brown so I had a tractor and no farm; but he was useful to plough the garden in his retirement. I even became a gardener and grew cabbages, etc. Mr Woggins of course came with us to our new home but his tractor days were over, although he spent hours just sitting in the tractor cab, no doubt just wishing and reminiscing about the old days. I sold the Scott motor cycle to Fred for £7 and bought a much more modern one, in fact a Douglas 350cc, for £25. It was not perfect but I purchased another one for £20 to use as spares. My need for modern and reliable transport was obvious, as I had to clock in at 8 am every morning and there was no way I was going to be late. The Douglas was a very reliable bike with good suspension but a pathetic performance after the Scott. To start his retirement my father bought a new Ford 5 cwt van so Betty, having just passed her driving test, had the Wolseley car to carry her to work in place of the old bicycle.

So here we were with a total change of life style, our free-and-easy ways gone perhaps forever. Even our humour and laughter changed; we now obtained more from the television and less from life and probably we were the worse for it; in any case we were getting older and as one does one's outlook on life changes.

My new job was fascinating. Getting a job card from Ben each morning, not knowing until that moment where I might be going that day; preparing the parts I might need; driving anything from a few miles to perhaps eighty or ninety; meeting new people, maybe grumpy farmers who regarded me as someone costing them money. In the long days of summer there was nearly always a good welcome; usually I had been called in because the harvest had come to a stop until I had the machine repaired. Cripps covered a large area and often I did not arrive home until perhaps 10 or 11 in the evening, and then might have another job awaiting to attend in the morning, leaving home as early as 7 am on occasions. The depot closed at 6 pm so if I had not returned to base by that time the journey home was made in the van. Of course these long hours meant there were plenty of overtime payments in my wage packet. I had a basic wage of £12 per week working from 8 am to 5.30 pm and until 12 noon on Saturday, but often I could have £20 or so in the little brown envelope we all looked forward to receiving each week, and with Betty's wages as well we were able to save quite a bit of money as time went on.

This summer work was so interesting to me, who had been limited in my mechanical ambitions to repairing our own or other people's used machinery. To have almost always a new or nearly new machine to attend to was indeed a pleasure – I could almost have paid them to let me do it. We were mostly dealing with the B45 baler, of which almost 100 were sold each year at that time; then there was the B55 with a powerful Armstrong Siddeley engine mounted over the bale chamber; and later in the year we had the B64 combine to handle. If you add to these the machines sold in the previous years you will not be surprised to hear that just four fitters were kept on the run all summer. It was great. Many were the hours spent sitting on the bale chamber watching the knotter and trying to establish what caused it to mistie every now and again. All this time great clouds of dust were being blown into my face, hair covered in dust, dusty cobwebs hanging from my eyelashes, dust and chaff up my nose, and worst of all the bits of grass, hay or straw that found their way down my back to itch all day long. Eventually one gets used to it and with a good look around the machine one can do various jobs that mean this dusty riding can be cut to a minimum but in the end there is no substitute for hands-on repairs. Of the B55 balers we sold one year, four never tied knots reliably. Another fitter and I both rode for hours on the bale chambers trying to isolate the problem, until one day a letter from I.H. told us to look for a certain piece of the machine being 2 inches shorter than it should be . . . *There* was the problem solved! But why had I not spotted it and why were we not told about it sooner? All part of the joys of agricultural

Ploughing match with a Messrs Cripps tractor in 1958

The Fordson forty-foot tower

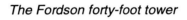

The fingertip Dexta

Mr Woggins

Bill

Springtime spraying. Note the home-made cab

Arthur and the demonstration van

Ambaston village as the floodwaters rose. Brook Farm is to the extreme right

Betty ready for the road on the Douglas motorcycle in 1959. (Yes, she did use the bike.)

Arthur with the radio tractor control box in Sweden in 1960

machinery, I am afraid. These memories of harvesting are brought clearly back every time I hear the hit song 'Magic Moments', which was at its height of popularity at that time and everyone seemed to be whistling or singing it. Very appropriate: they are indeed magic moments when you clean your hands in a harvest field and can see the farmer happily going around on his tractor and know his harvest is now on course again.

Our customers were a varied cross section of humanity. One farmer in north Derbyshire who had quite a lot of I.H. equipment seemed to have a police car there every time I visited him, usually with officers sitting in the kitchen drinking tea. Often I would share this with them, always joking together. I never asked why they were so often in evidence – sometimes it is better to keep your own council. Other farmers might arrive on an old tractor, often bringing a drink of tea and a bite with the invitation to 'have a break, lad'. Sometimes a well-dressed gentleman might arrive in his Jaguar and with an 'Oh, you're not finished yet then', drive away to pastures new. Others might offer an invitation to eat with them when the job was finished, and as I might have a two-hour drive home these invitations were gratefully received; often these families might have an attractive daughter (and in the remote parts of the eastern counties perhaps unattached), so I soon got into the way of saying something along the lines of 'I must not eat too much – my wife will have dinner ready when I get home', or 'I will get shot when my wife sees the state of my shirt'. One lady, who ran a 150-acre farm and whose father had now died, always drove the tractor when I visited to repair the baler. Usually it was hot and she would bring a drink into the field, always wearing the same clothes, a kind of uniform consisting of Land Girl-type brown bib and brace overalls with a short-sleeved blouse. The interesting thing was that the overalls were the kind that had side openings to give access to a pocket in the trousers usually worn underneath; but this rather attractive lady (possibly in her late twenties) did not wear trousers underneath the overalls on hot days – so whilst one repaired the baler a considerable area of white knickers and flesh would flash before one's eyes . . . Luckily I am not the sort who may be tempted! One day we had a real problem with the baler and I rode for possibly half an hour on it, in the process becoming covered in dust due to dry hay that had probably been overmade. Eventually I was satisfied all was well and stopped the forward motion, with rivers of sweat running down my face, covered in dust and with itchy bits all down my back. She looked at me and said 'Oh, you poor man! Come to the farm and whilst I make a drink you can have a bath.' I politely refused and so I never discovered if her bathroom door had a lock on it. Should I have found out? What do you think?

One particular day I left home early, drove south to Uppingham in Rutland to start off a new B64 combine, then to Burton upon Trent to repair a PTO shaft on a baler and afterwards up to Bamford to attend a knotter problem on another baler. At 4.30 pm I rang Ben to let him know where I was located and he informed me there was a very irate customer near Skegness who had been waiting all day for attention. Ben suggested I visit him early next morning but I volunteered to go that evening and left Ben to inform him I would be there about 7.30 pm. I was made very welcome and finished the repair at 9.30 ready for the two-hour drive home. Such a day with its 350 miles of driving was not so unusual and the experience stood me in good stead in later years with another company when I would expect to average 2000 miles each week.

The B64 combine I had started off that same morning I regarded as being an obsolete design. That was before I had used one. It needed a tractor to tow it around the field and only took a six-foot cut of the standing corn. Compared to the Massey Harris self-propelled machine which would take a ten- or twelve-foot cut, it did indeed seem obsolete; but when using it one found that because the threshing part was as wide as the cut it was almost impossible to overfeed the B64, whilst the Massey, although cutting maybe ten feet, could not take the crop so quickly owing to the threshing part on it being only four and a half feet wide. It is quite possible that the Massey would cut as much in a day as the B64 but it always seemed the B64 cut more because it travelled much faster – an illusion that sells things. The B64 had one main advantage, in my opinion, in that it could handle the wet and green undergrowth of so many English crops, whereas the Massey was probably designed for the short clean straw of the prairies. This ability to travel fast and cut and digest almost anything gave the B64 some problems; it was perhaps susceptible to breakages due to going too fast over rough ground and I have spent many miserable and cold winter days crawling into a B64 and scraping dried mud and general deposits from the inside of its guts which had accumulated owing to its ability to pass though the most awful wet crops imaginable.

After our harvest adventures the autumn came and with it the ploughing matches and tractor demonstrations, work that I loved. It was wonderful to have new tractors and machinery to prepare and use: to take a new tractor from stock, prepare it, polish it, clean all the chrome bits with petrol to remove all the preservative, make sure all the controls worked freely and smoothly, fill with fuel, water ballast the tyres, adjust tyre pressures and in general leave no stone unturned to make sure our scheme of taking a tractor on demonstration to a farm with the intention of selling it and leaving it there was achieved. We did not always sell but it was unusual for us to return a muddy tractor to the depot for me to wash and clean ready for the next demonstration. This proved a busy time – perhaps three or four demonstrations a week along with the ploughing matches of which we were winning more than perhaps was our share. Early in this autumn International Harvester announced to the sales department that they were introducing a new tractor bigger than the B250 which was our mainstay of sales, so our sales staff were invited to attend an introduction event, and quite out of the blue I was invited as well, although I was a fitter and not belonging to the sales side. Presumably someone thought it would be good for the organisation if I were to attend and learn from the I.H. specialists how to demonstrate the new beast.

This was the first time I had seen a works presentation. Later I was to be involved in organising such events and thus see them from another angle. This first one was very impressive, from the cocktail reception, sales manager's spiel, to a film show and finally a working field demonstration, meant to prove all other tractors would not sell now we had our new model available. Even if it did cost 15 per cent more than the most popular tractor already on the market, they tried to convince us that we had only to demonstrate it to eager farmers to sell the thing. But of course life it not like that.

Some days later the first of the new tractors, designated the B450, arrived covered so the public could not see it until announcement day, when demonstrations and nation-wide advertising would give impact over the whole country to a new sales drive to sell I.H. equipment. The tractor was carefully unloaded and hidden in a shed until the manufacturer's representative arrived to instruct the service personnel on its inner organs.

The day of the announcement came. We had selected a field to demonstrate which had a pronounced slope. Having watched the works demonstrators using the tractors at the introduction we formed the impression that these must be supermen with specially deformed left legs to enable the clutch pedal to be pressed, with rupture-proof stomach muscles so the gear lever could be prised out of one gear in preparation to engage another, and perhaps lead-lined eardrums to deaden the noise produced by the diesel injectors (which seemed to be injecting shot onto a tin roof with a demented blacksmith working overtime underneath it). Apart from this it seemed to be a good tractor. The sloping field had been selected to show off the long-stroke engine pulling hard at low revs as well as the tremendous traction we were assured was easily available from the large-diameter rear wheels.

Our tractor was indeed quite a goer and impressed the visitors quite as much as the free refreshments did. The local lads turned up in force and the machine stood the strain of successively suffering butchers, idiots and bigheads in the seat, proving at the end of the day unbreakable. Two days and much rain later we were summoned to a farm to prove our tractor was indeed a world-beater and invited to leave it there if it could prove its worth, being assured the cheque book was ready and a new refill fitted to the farmer's pen. Arriving with our four-furrow plough we were set to plough an undulating field. It was certainly very wet but a reasonable start was made. After a couple of rounds the farmer suggested we start to plough properly, indicating that his grandfather ploughed deeper than us using a donkey. Getting the required depth was quite a problem and after adjustments, suggestions of all kinds, and much squelching of mud, we were amused to see a very keen sales manager arrive in suede shoes. We finally got under way at nearly double the depth but suffering some wheelspin which I was desperately trying to disguise. Halfway across the field we hit a slight depression in the surface and soon it was obvious that all forward motion was lost so I stopped before we were disastrously bogged. Now I had some experience driving tractors in wet conditions and I knew we had a definite problem. The sales manager, getting excited and perhaps seeing the farmer's cheque book fading in the rain, jumped on the footplate, mud nearly up to his knees (suit definitely second-hand by this time) and suggested we lift the plough and drive out of the bog. The engine was running so he pulled up the hydraulic lever to lift the plough. Nothing happened to the plough, it just stayed in the ground, but the tractor was gently pushed further into the mire. I stopped the engine and we looked at one another in the ensuing silence. The farmer grinned at us and asked if we would like to try another field and for God's sake use a real plough in that one. All we had to do was get the tractor out of the bog, so we dug, spun the wheels, dug some more and stirred up the soil until it was quite fluid. Then the sales rep suggested we borrow the farmer's Cletrac crawler to pull out our fine new tractor. That idea was short-lived – the farmer pointed to a stake sticking out of the field some way off, claiming that it was the Cletrac exhaust, all that could be seen of the Cletrac since it had sunk out of sight two weeks before. We removed the plough with difficulty and in about half an hour were ready to try the farmer's plough in a rather steep field across the road.

His plough was a single-furrow deep digger, trailed of course, so at last we were able to show off our new tractor to its full (noisy) potential. Ploughing 14 inches deep and 18 inches wide it produced a very satisfying job. The tractor with one wheel in the furrow 14 inches below the other one made for an uncomfortable ride but showed off the differential lock to perfection. Two hours later we set off for our depot without a tractor but carrying a substantial cheque.

About this time our beloved B250 was replaced with the B275 tractor – just a little jazzed up and had a bit more power but basically the same machine. Our sales manager, now with a clean suit and a nice warm office, gave us a real I.H. pep talk but said nothing we did not know; but then sales managers, at that time, were paid for that sort of thing, which usually meant very little. I felt a growing understanding of these antics and grew to dislike their obvious manoeuvring to impress both their superiors and their lackeys such as me. Our sales representatives were much closer to my estimation of people who live in the real world, probably because most days they would be brought down to earth with a bump when dealing with farmers, they of the land who knew exactly when being sold a line of 'bull' and just how to squash it. This sales manager's pep talk gave me much food for thought. I was not sure whether I intended to remain a fitter for ever; perhaps I could do a sales job; after all, for over a year now I had seen the highs and lows of our sales reps' lives, particularly at demonstrations on the farms, and I figured that in spite of the lows it was a better life than breathing baler dust, freezing in a farmyard over a winter service or pressure-washing a muddy tractor in the cold. In the end I decided it was unlikely my education would be enough to satisfy Cripps that they would wish to move me to the sales department. Big companies usually go for fine educational paperwork even if the owners of it are educated idiots (and, believe me, I have seen more than my share of those). So I got on with my life as a fitter which, in any case, I was thoroughly enjoying and believed I was good at. Little did I know the seeds of ambition had been set and in a year's time I would have moved on from the I.H. products I was so proud of.

9

THE winter of 1958, like the previous one, I enjoyed very much. I worked less overtime but this meant that Betty and I could enjoy the company of friends better than we had ever been able to do. We spent a wonderful Christmas with our landlord and his family, visiting our families and friends so much so that the winter soon passed and I was again touring around the East Midlands in the van visiting good-natured farmers who perhaps gave me a net of carrots, enough to feed a herd of donkeys, some potatoes or eggs or sometimes a few cabbages. We lived very well and enjoyed life to the full.

The B275 tractors we had sold soon began to give problems as the spring work got under way. Blown cylinder head gaskets were the problem; I changed two one day and could not believe it when a few days later the problem recurred. I was so confident of my ability to do this repair that I found it difficult to accept I had failed. Then instructions came from I.H. that every tractor we had sold needed the head gasket to be changed, as a helicoil insert was not long enough and must be changed for a longer one. End of problem and I felt renewed confidence as a fitter.

The summer came and with it the dirt of harvest and the pressure of burning up the roads again to keep abreast of all the work. Towards the end of the summer an advertisement was placed in the press by Ford Motor Company asking for anyone interested to apply for a post of temporary tractor demonstrator. Betty and I studied this and discussed it quite deeply. In the end we decided it must be investigated and an application was sent off. This meant a lot of heart-searching for both of us: I because of my devotion to International Harvester products and Betty because we both felt it likely we should have to be parted for some of the time. What little I knew of Fordson Major and Dexta tractors I did not particularly like, but realised any progress must be good; so when I received a letter asking me to attend the Ford Mechanised Training Centre at Boreham in Essex we both began to take the situation much more seriously.

I arrived in Essex to be suitably impressed with Boreham House and its staff. The facilities were tremendous: sales and service instruction rooms, workshop facilities and a cinema. I was told this was to be a sales promotion venture of short-term duration but it was possible that a very few people would be retained by the company at the end of it and others were likely to be placed with the dealer network. The rewards appeared meagre at first – basic pay £9 per week; a cost of living and transport allowance of £15 per week seemed to improve matters, but I had to travel around the country on this amount for a week and find four nights' accommodation. During my interview I had been impressed with the Ford facilities and met some very pleasant people who seemed to know what they were talking about. I hoped that I had also given this impression.

Some time later a letter arrived offering me a temporary position as a tractor demonstrator along with an agreement to sign and return. My days with International Harvester equipment and Messrs Cripps were almost over. The managing director summoned me to his office and understanding my motives wished me well and asked me to contact him if I needed a job at any time in the future. I thought this was an extremely good and gentlemanly gesture, which helped to soften my regret at leaving an excellent company. Saying goodbye to the friends I had made, especially Ben, was hard but I am pleased to say we are still friends although not in regular contact.

Simply to write about these events now seems quite tame but it was a very fundamental step to take at that time. I had a well-paid, enjoyable, permanent job with a good company and now I was giving this up to gamble on a temporary position becoming permanent, and with no certainty that it would be a job as enjoyable as the one I had relinquished. The requirement was that I should attend Boreham for three weeks' training, the first two of which were to be without a break and very concentrated. This of course meant that Betty and I were to be parted for the first time since our wedding ten years before and, worse still, Betty had to stay in a remote cottage by herself. As it happened these were minor problems compared with the lengthy partings we were to have in future years, but at that time two weeks seemed like a lifetime, though not so bad for me, as I had the excitement of going to a new job and working with new people.

Arriving at Boreham House on Sunday at 6 pm I found friendly people and warm surroundings. There were nine other temporary staff and a few Ford staff, so most of the evening was taken up with chat and familiarising with one another. There was a large games room and a bar, as I understand it the only bar on any Ford premises anywhere in the world. (Why this should be so I am not sure. Henry Ford was not given to taking alcohol and certainly was a strict non-smoker, so why a bar at Boreham? Maybe it dated from the time before the house was occupied by Ford.) Our accommodation was of the dormitory type, a few people sharing a room, but after our cottage without mains services it was most luxurious especially to have central heating. So our first evening together passed; we were full of hope and expectation, not knowing what the future might bring.

After breakfast next morning we were welcomed to the Ford family by the sales promotion manager, Mr Peter Forsyth, shown a film of Ford and Fordson operations world wide . . . and the quiet brainwashing had started. After coffee we met Boreham staff face to face for the first time on an instructor-to-worker relationship. A pep talk was given by Mr Bob Turner, manager of Boreham at that time and a man whom I came to have a great deal of respect for. He had a great product knowledge and a serious and searching personality but could lead or join the evening relaxation in the bar when our duties permitted, which, I must say, was not often. Bob Turner was the owner of the most piercing eyes I have ever met, eyes that seemed to cut through your head; well, we all came to know them as our turn would come to answer his questions on items of product knowledge that he considered we should have gleaned. Senior instructor was Doug Blair, another dyed-in-the-wool Ford man and not just a rabid enthusiast for his product but a man who could put over the product knowledge he so sincerely believed in. The other member of staff we were closely involved with was Ken Rawlings, whose responsibilities in this team of people who were trying to turn us from raw recruits into people who might represent Ford with a modicum of expertise was to oversee the outside and field work. As years went by Ken and his wife Nita became good friends and gave both Betty and me a great deal of help. (Regrettably my nomadic life has meant we did not keep in close touch with them but I hope we can still number them as our friends.) There are many names I could mention and perhaps should but it would not add to this story and in no way would I wish to embarrass colleagues and friends who may now be in the higher echelons of business and who might be caused embarrassment by my ramblings about their humbler beginnings.

We were now really back to school – but school was never as interesting as this. Notebooks, desks, study, even to the evening instruction periods which meant we were lucky if there was time to sneak a quick half hour in the bar – there were so many things to read and swot up for the next day's operations. After a few day's intensive study we were presented with new white overalls with 'Fordson' branded across the back. We were getting prouder by the day. Also we had a tool kit each, in a Fordson branded holdall – and woe betide anyone who lost anything. We were now ready to take to the fields.

In case you think I am harping on about this period, remember (as far as I have read) before now no one has ever written about this sort of intensive training and 'brainwashing'. Most people seeing a tractor and its demonstrator at some event probably think 'That fellow has a good job'; well, maybe he has – but I must tell you it does not happen by accident! There were about thirty tractors at Boreham, both Dextas and Majors. We were split into pairs, one with a Dexta and the other with a Major, so we could change over when required and thus gain experience of both types. We were also responsible for the wellbeing of our tractors and the presentation of them each morning having cleaned and restored them from the previous day's adventures. They were almost new tractors and we were expected to keep them in this new condition irrespective of the previous day's mud or damage. I really believe they deliberately took us to the dirtiest part of the training acreage so the tractors were really dirty and well used. The autumn rain did not help either.

In case you think this admittedly rather glamorous life was easy, let me correct this fallacy. One day when we returned to the yard with our equipment just as it was going dark and drizzling with rain, we were told to cut our meal time to a minimum as there was to be an inspection of our tractors at 8 pm 'and they had better be perfect or else'. Bob Turner eventually inspected our equipment and looking back I now believe he had a lot of quiet amusement in giving each of us scathing criticism and a list of defects such as mud on the inside of the wheels or dirt on the underside of the lift arms, paint worn off the footplates, dirty tyres, etc. When inspection was finished each of us had a long list of defects to correct and because the training schedule was not to be interrupted we must present our tractors for inspection in as-new condition next morning at 9 am. It was suggested we organise shift work through the night to rectify matters. So we were quickly learning to prepare and keep our equipment in top grade order – a habit which has never left me, so even now I am not happy competing in a ploughing match if my tractor is dirty.

As in all big companies there were two facets to my new life: a deadly serious and viciously competitive side to the learning process, as Ford mercilessly assessed our potential and let our gradings and achievements be known, and a social side, when the Boreham staff would join us in the bar for a drink or a game of table tennis and sometimes the alcoholic game of 'cardinal puff'. This soon taught me to drink and enjoy alcohol which, apart from the odd half pint, I had never done before. Even in this social side I had the feeling we were still being assessed.

Out in the yard was a man named Claud Church, who looked after equipment in general. Although the service staff at Boreham had terrific product knowledge it was not part of their job to carry out repairs; Claud did most of this kind of work and had a real store of knowledge and stories. He soon became very popular with all the temporary staff, always willing to help, battered trilby hat stuck to the back of his head, fag usually dangling from his lips. I bet he had no qualifications but if you needed to know *anything* about tractors he was the best man to ask. I remember one of the Major tractors was almost imposs-ible to start so was very rarely used, Claud was always going to get the pump and injectors set up correctly; he thought this was the problem, but to this point had not done it. On this tractor was mounted a Holman com-pressor and we were wanting to use it as part of a road drill instruction course during our general training. I was delegated to start the tractor and prepare it for use. At this time I was unaware of its stubborn starting characteristics (indeed the Fordson Major is, in my opinion, the best starting diesel one could wish to own), so I was suitably surprised when it failed to start the first time the engine turned over. Claud quickly put his head out of the workshop shouting to me to leave it or I would have the battery flat. He quickly came over and, lifting the bonnet, poked an oil can into a hole. He must have put it in the rubber air tube feeding the engine air from the air cleaner. I soon found out that the oil can contained petrol. 'Right, turn the engine over.' As I did so he gave the Major several lusty squirts of petrol, it started instantly, but the smoke and the metallic noises just had to be heard to be believed. 'Cor, jest like the effing bells o' St Mary's, ennit?' he shouted over the expensive noises the poor Major was producing. What a character! Alas no longer

105

with us; in fact colourful types like Claud seem to be a dying breed.

As the end of our second week approached we were assessed, reassessed, pressurised, worked almost to death – and enjoyed every minute of it. Even to me, used to doing dealer demonstrations, it was an eye-opener to see the standard of skill and the way staff were trained by a main manufacturer to attain it. I had learned a great deal not just about demonstrating tractors but also about training, although at this time I was not so much aware of this newly acquired skill; not until later when a dealer asked me to give his sales staff a two-day course on demonstrating techniques did I realise what hidden skill I had gained. I feel sure all of us were proud of what had been achieved and proud to be part of Ford. It would be hard to have to say goodbye at the end of the six months.

During our training period there were four Ford Trader trucks parked at Boreham announcing to the world from large headboards that they were Fordson Tracteuropa demonstration units. We all looked upon these units with envy, especially when told that they had just returned from a tour of Scandinavia and Germany. Our ambitions were growing.

On the Friday of our second week, before we were due to go home for a weekend break, we were assembled and given our objective for the six-month period we were due to serve. This was to visit Fordson main dealers and assist in doing any demonstrations that came up during our stay there or perhaps visit other dealers if required. All our movements were to be controlled by the Ford sales representative, later called area managers, to whose area we were to be allocated. We were also expected to provide extra back-up product knowledge to the dealer's own staff if needed on selected visits to customers. As usual in large organisations the vital bit of knowledge we needed – which area we were to work in – did not arrive for our Friday briefing but we were assured it was being posted to us from Dagenham that very afternoon and should reach us on Saturday morning, so with that we left for home, visiting wives and girl friends for the first time in two weeks. We were told to report back on Sunday evening and not to expect the next week to be any easier than the last two, but most of us had other things on our minds for the next few hours.

During the brief spell I had worked for Alfa Laval ten or so years previously it always gave me pleasure to let Betty open the letter telling us where our next job was to be. On the Saturday morning the letter came from Dagenham and, true to form, it was opened by Betty. 'Can you believe it?' she said. 'The Isle of Man is part of your area.' In fact I had Cumberland, Westmorland, Northumberland, Durham, the Isle of Man and Northern Ireland – quite an area considering the number of Fordson main dealers it covered. My immediate boss was the area sales representative, Tom Birrel, who would arrange which dealers I was to visit. Sitting down and working all this out it seemed obvious that a motor cycle was neither able to carry my equipment nor represent a suitable image for the company, so off we went to Derby to see if other transport could be found. We were lucky: a Ford 5 cwt van was on offer at £105 and they even gave me £60 for the Douglas motor cycle. On Sunday morning we collected the van ready for the journey back to Boreham.

As I drove back I reflected on my new position, how only three years ago I had been working on the farm and now I was about to represent a major company like Ford in a large area of northern England and even to instruct

107

dealer staff, who up to this time I had regarded as the experts. Returning to Boreham was like going home, but we were soon brought down to earth. Each man was allocated an implement and told that on Tuesday we would visit the Smithfield Show, where we should get all the information available to prepare us to give a presentation on Wednesday to Bob Turner in the lecture room on that particular implement.

My subject was tractor-mounted loaders. This task worried me more than a little; never before had I been required to stand at a lectern and give a presentation to an assembled company and certainly not a company that included Bob Turner's piercing eyes. However, it had to be done and it went quite well, the experience standing me in good stead later with the dealers, especially on my first visit to a dealer in Carlisle when awful weather meant that the planned demonstration was cancelled and I was told to give the sales team a talk on demonstrating tractors and plough setting in particular. Afterwards I was congratulated and this made me reflect on the three weeks' training Ford had given us all which, I guess, money could not buy in such a concentrated time and to the standard they had used. All credit to those skilled instructors at Boreham.

Now my life revolved around Fordson Major and Dexta tractors and journeys up and down the roads leading to the North of England, up the A1 for the east side or the A6 for the west. There were no motorways at this time and I could sometimes have been found in the Ford van travelling (or perhaps queuing) in the middle of Doncaster at 6 am or Piccadilly in Manchester at a similar hour so I could arrive in perhaps Newcastle or Carlisle on time at 9 am. Usually travelling north on Monday morning and returning south Friday night, these could be rough old journeys in fog or snow, and rain was not a lot better.

But I was being educated. Messrs Crofts of Kendal attended a ploughing match and had a plot to plough with a Dexta. Their lorry was engaged in other work so I volunteered to drive the tractor and plough to the event. Setting out at 8 am I had not realised how far it was (or how cold – it was perishing!) and the journey was about thirty miles. After the plot was finished and many farmers had tried out the Dexta I had to drive it back to Kendal, but not before the match secretary had insisted I visit their church hall in the evening for what he called our 'Hedgehog Hotpot'. Those were long days and evenings (we often did farmer presentations after dusk) but great times and very enjoyable and I was gaining confidence all the time.

The visit to Northern Ireland came when Tom asked me to assist Messrs Coulters of Belfast in a drainage demonstration. The worst of the Troubles had not really started at that time – and what a wonderful place it turned out to be! I travelled overnight from Liverpool to Belfast without my van and was met off the boat by a salesman from Coulters and transported across the province to a little town called Limavady, booked into a hotel and then deposited in a wet low-lying area of black peaty soil to help set up the equipment for the next day's demonstration. Lunch time came quite quickly and we retired to the hotel. Now lunch with my new friends, I quickly realised, meant mostly Guinness, on rare occasions perhaps a sandwich but mostly Guinness, in pints. That is not to suggest they drank too much; just a few pints and then back to work maybe in half an hour or maybe two hours – who was to say? Sitting in the bar reading his newspaper a quite respectably dressed man put down his paper and walking over to the bar asked for a 'mountain dew'. He was given about half a tumbler of clear liquid from an unlabelled bottle taken from under the bar for two shillings. After our liquid lunch we returned to our bog and finished setting up the equipment, returning to the hotel after dark, cold and damp, when we found the gentleman still there. The mountain dew I decided was not something one might drink freely, as he was kneeling on the floor with his head on the seat of the chair fast asleep. We warmed ourselves partly with the roaring log and peat fire but mostly with the famous Blackbush whisky. Eventually our friend from the chair decided to awake and try to stand. This he managed after some failures and a few groans, and he wandered haphazardly across the room until he met a central supporting pillar which totally foxed him: he could find no way round it. Eventually some decent person steered him around the post and he made his way outside. So be warned: never drink 'mountain dew' from under the counter – stick to the one on the bar with a proper label on it!

The next day was fine and sunny but again very cold and we had a good demonstration. I worked a low-cost ditching attachment for the Dexta and next to me was a Leeford Ditcher mounted on a Fordson Major and operated by another visitor from England; as the Leeford worked the whole area around it shivered, water gurgled and I prepared to jump like a cricket if the ground gave way, but it never did. The day passed quickly and we were soon back in the bar. By now I had missed one night's sleep (on the boat), two lunches, 'enjoyed' a long night in the bar, and now decided that the English constitution – mine anyway – was not as resilient as the Irish one, so I would have a nice dinner and an early night. My friends were sorry about this because they had a drinking den up in the hills all lined up for the evening's entertainment. But it was no good. They eventually went off after a couple of beef sandwiches washed down with Guinness. I enjoyed a good dinner and night's sleep.

Next day we moved location to another bog. (They have plenty over there.) It was a late start; my friends were not so lively at breakfast but a good Guinness lunch seemed to perk them up no end and all was ready when darkness descended upon us . . . And so my life went on. I was by now thoroughly enjoying it and especially so the next week when it was decided I should visit a few of the retail dealers in Northern Ireland. These fellows were not used to getting any back-up from Dagenham and I was made very welcome indeed, very often living as one of the family. It was fine so long as you could drink the same as they did even, as in some cases, if it was only tea. It was vital over there to know what you were talking about; the people of the province take it as a personal affront if English companies send over someone who gives the impression that the Irish are not quite as intelligent as the English. Believe me, the normal Irish tractor man would hold his own in England with the best. How I thanked my stars for the intensive instruction Ford had given me; in the end my life was good and my confidence high because many of the people who had taken me around to their customers asked Tom when I would be returning.

As March came along and my six-month temporary period looked like coming to its end I began to consider the dealers I was visiting with a view to forming an opinion about building my personal future, since Ford were not showing any interest in it. During March I was again in Northern Ireland, in fact in Omagh with Eakins, who had an important ploughing match to attend. I had a wonderful time helping Fordson users get the best from

111

their tractors. A great deal of time was spent travelling between the site and Eakins' workshop. I had my van over there on this trip, collecting parts or modifying a plough share; heating it perhaps and giving a little more lift to the wing or a bit more penetration. All sorts of things the Irish do which very few ploughmen understand in England. The next day I was taken to visit a farmer who was having problems with his Major, by one of the representatives of Eakins (a man whom I totally lost track of until I saw he was ploughing in the world match in Sweden in 1993 and arranged to meet again). We did our best to solve the farmer's problem and were invited to stay for a 'bite'. How wonderful the Irish are, so hospitable and friendly! As we went to the house the rep whispered to me, 'You'll be having a shock here,' and sure enough I did. It was a small Irish farm and the house was typical of the era. We entered through a stable-type door into a kitchen–cum–living-room, quite large, with a beaten earth floor, a few chickens sharing it, a peat fire with its characteristic smell, a black cauldron hanging over it, a white-wood table and on each side of the fireplace a curtained bed on a wooden base. We had soup from the cauldron, home-made bread with cheese with a jug of beer or milkless tea if we wished to fill our glasses. The talk never stopped: ploughing, tractors, the price of crops, where was my home, etc, a really memorable meal in the most primitive circumstances – but oh, the conversation!

Returning to Eakins I found a message for me to telephone Dagenham as soon as possible. Could I report to the office at 9 am? Considering it was by now late afternoon this was not possible (but I often found office people have no knowledge of geography), so it was established that I would present myself one day later.

Catching the boat from Belfast that evening I was home in the afternoon and in Dagenham the next morning. The sales promotion office at that time was a collection of wooden buildings on the dockside at Dagenham and this was where I reported to. I saw two supervisors and three managers and was then ushered into the presence of the top man, Mr W. Batty. I found them all very pleasant men but they all asked me the same questions and then told me I could go back to Eakins.

Two weeks later all trainees received a message to return to Boreham. We all arrived hoping against hope we should be made aware of our future in the Ford organisation. As you may realise we were together for the first time since we had joined our various areas and so the talk was continuous. Many tales were told but I will repeat only one. This concerned a demonstrator who arrived with his dealer only to find the plough he was supposed to use had been left outside and was really rusty. There was no way it would perform in any satisfactory way like that, but this fellow was inventive so he sandpapered the worst of the rust off and, because this dealer had his premises close to the sea, he decided to take the tractor and plough down to the beach and brighten the plough on the abrasive sand. This worked well so, feeling pleased with himself, he decided to drive out into the sea and clean the tractor. He had not checked the fuel. The engine stopped as the water came up to footplate level and the tide was coming in . . . I am led to believe that only a trained athlete could have run the distance to the dealer's and back with a can of fuel in the time available, but with a supreme effort the demonstrator made it.

This visit to Boreham was different; no instruction, but a briefing that the company was to arrange a public

113

demonstration known as a Farming Fair at Wickhambrook in Suffolk and we were the 'fortunate' staff to do the work, under a sales promotion superviser called John Prentice, a canny Scot and, as we found, nobody's fool but a generous and likeable character. We were now involved in something totally new and in addition were to use the four Tracteuropa trucks and equipment. We really began to feel like manufacturer's demonstrators at last; we had floodlights, cinema, public-address equipment, cutaway tractors, radio-controlled tractors and other manufacturers' staff who would be looking after their own equipment being used on our tractors. We had to mark out a plot for each piece of equipment.

When we were well on the way with our preparations half a day was given over to learning a routine for the Dexta. This was designed to take place in a small ring. Over the public-address system came a commentary, and the driver (of neat appearance and dressed in white overalls) pointed out various features of the tractor – good access to the oil-filler, battery, radiator filler, etc – in coordination with the speaker. Also a special cultivator was fitted to the tractor to show how easy it was to attach implements, and the reversing to the implement had to be perfect; it was not acceptable at any time for the driver not to stop precisely so each arm and the top link could be attached easily and in seconds – it was quite out of the question to have to move the implement to achieve this. We then had to demonstrate the two hydraulic systems of the Dexta. Another feature of the Dexta, the large footplates, were shown, so whilst the commentor was speaking of these I, wearing a pair of stage boots of bright yellow and black (which must have been size 24, in fact I could get them over my own shoes), had to run to the tractor, falling over in the process just to emphasise the

114

size of my feet, and whilst the commentator rattled on about how farmers with even the largest feet would find the Dexta easy to drive, I had to mount the tractor and drive around the ring.

With the plots all marked out and a tractor and its implement in place at the end of each plot, we were grilled about how the villainous young farmers would put on the headlights and run the battery down and how we must always carry a spanner in our pockets to fit or remove a battery wire and immobilise the tractor, how we must suspect the visitors might switch off the fuel just to see our embarrassment when the tractor stopped halfway across the field. . . . As the loudspeaker van approached the tractor we were going to demonstrate, it was our job to be certain that not only would it start when instructed but that it would keep running. I noticed on a film on television one night that Harry Ferguson expected his demonstrators to line up their implements along the edge of the plots so a bullet could be fired through all the top link attachment holes and how each tractor had to be attached as the implement was going to be demonstrated. I must say he either did not have many implements to demonstrate or the field was as level as a bowling green. We had a tractor to each implement and hoped the show would run like clockwork. It almost always did so.

Here I was able to drive a Doe Triple D tractor for the first time and also many other things I had not used before. It was so interesting and instructional. After the field was cleared we returned all the equipment to Boreham. We had had a wonderful three weeks out in the country working long hours and very hard, so now we were in our last week of employment and no indication of our future had been given to us. As we parked the

115

Tracteuropa trucks we found four new ones now also parked up. How nice to have this sort of money to spend just demonstrating tractors! These new trucks, similar in appearance to the old ones but how smart and bright they looked with new plastic coated tilts and bright new paintwork – just wonderful. How we longed to be a permanent part of this life! With two days to go before our temporary employment was to end we were called together and some members sent off to dealers for interviews but three of us were held back to prepare the new trucks, filling up with fuel, checking and polishing.

10

A few days later I was again summoned to Dagenham and asked whether I had a passport. I had none, so I was sent to Ford photographic department to have a picture taken, and then filled in an application form and was told they had a nice little job for me – in Sweden! 'How long shall I be there?' I asked. 'Oh, possibly until October', I was told; 'anyway, go and have a couple of days at home and return on Thursday morning for your passport. We hope to send you off on Saturday.' Driving home I could not help wondering what Betty might say to her husband just leaving at two days' notice. I cannot say she was overjoyed but accepted that we might be on to a good thing – after all, how could they not employ me if I was to spend most of the summer on assignment overseas? And they had promised two weeks' holiday in July.

Returning to Dagenham after a rather short but very pleasant break I asked if this meant they were finally employing me. It appeared that this was indeed possible but that the current year's budget did not stretch to allow more staff, so I would have to be temporary for a little longer yet. The passport was ready in the office – how these companies can move when required! – and I was sent to the branch of Barclays bank located near the factory entrance with a note for them to issue me with traveller's cheques. I was required to sign for the money and sign each cheque in the presence of the manager, who finally said, 'Thank you, Mr Battelle, that makes £1500'. To say it almost took my breath away is an understatement. To suddenly have that amount of money and still not officially work for the company was unbelievable. By now I was coming in for considerable ribbing from all and sundry about spending the summer in the land of free love, and many were the sly remarks that came my way. I also now had an air ticket to Stockholm. I could hardly believe it: six months after working for a dealer, here I was with a weekly wage of £9 and £1500 and an air ticket in my pocket. A crazy world!

We drove the new trucks to Millwall dock so they could be loaded for shipping to Ford in Stockholm. Two of our team were to travel with them and three of us were to fly from London airport. As we arrived at the dock there was a short delay, during which we were approached by the foreman of the loading team of dockers to say he liked our new trucks and felt it would be a pity if they were scratched during the loading process; he suggested that it would be better if spreaders were used to stop the sling rubbing on our new paintwork, but they would have to fetch them from the store and this he felt was worth an extra payment to the loading team. A £5 note changed hands so all was well. I was just having my view confirmed that after so many dock strikes in post-war years, dock unions received their just rewards for the wildcat behaviour and complete disregard for the workers' wellbeing, now resulting in the closure of the docks and loss of so many jobs. This opinion was borne out on a later visit to Millwall docks when I had to cough up £5 to release a crate of spares or wait until after lunch, another three hours at least. Thank goodness the London dock system is now almost dead. Perhaps some of these dubious characters are now where they deserve to be, on the dole.

With my two colleagues I proceeded to Heathrow

airport for my first flight. What luxury it was, much more so in those days than it is now. Or is it just that comfortable conditions for passengers have become routine? Anyway, we arrived in Stockholm in good order and had enjoyed our flight to this great city and the views over the water as we came in to land at Bromma airport. Such clear water and so many islands, equalling one, I was told, for every citizen of the capital city. We were met by our team leader, Henry Reynolds. Henry seemed to me the typical English gentleman, wonderful accent, totally in command, giving us all confidence. I developed a great deal of respect for Henry. I suppose I needed someone to look up to; I was after all out of my depth here; so many things had happened so quickly. Henry took us to our hotel, The Grand, just across the water from the royal palace, never had I experienced luxury like this. We spent three days here, a far cry from mending dirty tractors or balers in a freezing stackyard back home in England. After two days our trucks arrived on the boat from Millwall dock also carrying the two members of our team who had made the journey on the boat, and we now could start the preparations and briefing for our tour of Sweden. We made seats for the back of the Thames van so we could transport our team around and cleaned the trucks after the sea journey (this work being undertaken in the factory of Ford Sweden in Stockholm).Our tour was to cover the length of the country from Malmö in the south as far as Luleå in the north. The intention was to drive most of the tractors from site to site by road, carrying other goods on trailers or the few trucks that were available, ours in any case being fully loaded.

The schedule called for two demonstrations each week but the first one, at Uppsala, just north of Stockholm, allowed a full week's preparation as a settling-in

119

exercise. The tractors and trucks were all lined up outside the factory ready for our ceremonial departure (press publicity arranged by Ford) and a police escort shepherded us through the city, not helping the traffic situation at all. The English contingent had five vehicles and six drivers so I was asked to drive a Fordson Major the forty or so miles to the site. This was my first taste of driving a tractor with a safety cab. Sweden of course is a very safety-conscious country but I have to say these early cabs must have deafened more drivers than they saved lives. The one I drove, of course in top gear flat out, so the noise level would be at its highest. Before we reached the outskirts of the city my head was singing and the heat in the cab was torrid. Luckily the Swedish tractors all had a square removable roof panel in the top of the cab, to enable the drivers to escape if the tractor broke through the ice when working on the frozen lakes as many of them did in the winter, many tractors spending the better part of the winter working in the forests and using frozen lakes and rivers as roads. I removed the roof panel and could then stand up with my head out of the cab top, on straight roads it was possible to steer with my foot and this fine, cool observation point enabled me to finish the journey in comfort.

During this journey our whole cavalcade was led, as it was on all the journeys, by the Swedish demonstration van fitted with a very loud public-address system, usually playing loud pop music as we travelled, the hit in Sweden that summer seemed to be 'Seven Little Girls in the Back Seat', or maybe that was the loudest record; anyway I hate to think what the wildlife including deer and elk thought about this noise echoing through the silent Swedish forests, but it certainly brought out the population of the towns and villages as we passed.

It is not my intention to spell out in detail each demonstration we did, in fact about 36 in all, but some things remain firmly fixed in my mind and some of these I will recall. Arriving at our site just to the north of Uppsala we found several units had been shipped direct to the site, a couple of Fordson based loaders, a Shawnee Poole dumper and a Triple D tractor, to be correct a Doe Dual Drive made by the large Fordson dealer in Essex. This tractor, for those who do not know it, is two Fordson tractors coupled together as one unit; the front axles are taken off and the front of the rear tractor, on which the driver sits, is mounted on a support on the rear of the front tractor. Now it seemed to me that in Sweden at that time there was a shortage of really big ploughs because the Doe was towing two ploughs one behind the other and connected to the tractor with hydraulic pipes so the controls could be worked from the tractor seat. We now had a writhing mass of machinery which some poor soul was trying to plough with, keeping the furrows straight and the ends neat. But this problem was as nothing when the time came to take the tractor away at the end of the demonstration. The driver proudly set off down the road concentrating very hard, I am sure; he was manfully trying to get the tractor into a higher gear, control the throttle and keep the quick-reacting power steering under control. Keeping the tractor travelling in a straight line was never easy at the best of times but now he had to allow for the two ploughs following. I believe this was new territory for him because whilst looking forward in his concentration he was not aware of a slight waver in the travel of the two ploughs which built up until there was a violent whiplash effect, the vibration eventually drawing his attention to the ploughs which were by this time whiplashing from one side of the road to the other.

121

Approaching drivers were taking to the grass verge in a desperate attempt to avoid this metallic whip, only one ran in the ditch and we soon had a tractor to pull him out. How pleased I was not to speak or understand Swedish!

We carried with us a quantity of maroons. How we ever managed to import so much explosive into a peace-loving country like Sweden I will never know. The purpose of these very powerful maroons was to attract the attention of the public to a point in the field where we hoped to start our demonstrations. Of course they fascinated me and very soon I was designated the one to let them off. This meant digging a hole to set the heavy tube in before dropping the maroon down it and lighting the fuse. The resulting explosion shook the ground and threw up the main body of the thing so just as the crowd were looking what on earth had caused this explosion the second explosion occurred high in the air, a much sharper crack this one and fairly visible so the crowd was brought to the point in the field where we wanted them. We decided (guess who was the ringleader) that the explosion in the air ought to be more visible to aid the spectators' awareness of the starting point so in our 'expert' way we decided to enhance it.

Now it so happened that we carried with us equipment for a balloon race, so that visitors could fill in a form, tie an addressed card to a balloon and launch it into the air. In due course the card returned from the furthest distance would win a prize for the person who sent the card and the one who found it. We provided the cards and balloons but Ford Sweden provided the gas, which was obtained locally. The cylinder we had on site contained hydrogen and I had been telling everyone that it was very dangerous. Though I believe it is against the law to use this gas for balloons we were doing so, often filling balloons and putting them in the van to give to the kids back in town. In an attempt to prove how dangerous they were I tied a balloon to a fence rail, borrowed a lighted cigarette and held it towards the balloon, being sure to turn my head away. When the heat contacted the balloon and melted the rubber there was a sheet of flame, burning the hairs off my arm and scorching my overall. No more inflated balloons were carried in cars or given to children, but already the Ford tractor Demonstration team had become the fastest tiers of balloons in that part of the world.

It now struck me that if we could lift a maroon in the air with a few balloons we could achieve our aim of making the crowd-pulling explosion much more effective; there was also the possibility of a real flash of fire high in the air in addition to the bang. We must have been quite mad. By experimenting we found it took 35

Never use hydrogen in balloons!

gas filled balloons to lift a maroon, so we tied a maroon to this cluster and sent it aloft with the fuse burning underneath it. As it cleared some trees on the site a wind must have caught it, veering it towards the main road running alongside. The idea worked well: when the explosion came, now quite high up, the flash from the 35 balloons would have done credit to a space rocket. But we in our innocence − or criminal negligence − had forgotten the second explosion. The second part of the maroon fell into the main road and went off with another mighty explosion. Luckily the only car passing steered round it and just kept on driving, maybe a little harder than before. We ceased our experiments on maroons forthwith.

A few more demonstrations and we were beginning to settle down to the routine. It was hard work, particularly when we had three in a week, putting up twelve floodlights, making sure each one was positioned exactly in line, running out the wiring for them, setting up a central electric control box fed by our six-cylinder-engine-powered generator. We had to erect and blow up our 100-seat cinema (the pneumatic type of 'blow up', I hasten to add). We carried a cutaway Dexta mounted on a plinth with a cover to erect over it. There was the balloon race of course.

We also had a 40-foot tower with a flashing light on top and what every-one called the fingertip. This was a full-size Dexta tractor with a large fibre-glass hand underneath it and the extended index finger pointing to the sky; on this the Dexta balanced vertically on the edge of its front tyre. It required an electric supply because it revolved on its balanced position. The radio-controlled tractor was always a most popular display, contributing greatly to the film and radio coverage we obtained. This tractor had caused us some problems in Stockholm

124

because the safety people insisted no tractor could operate in Sweden without a safety cab, a ruling which of course we ridiculed and argued strongly against partly because a safety cab meant it was not a remote-controlled tractor at all as it implied someone had to drive it, but mostly because a cab would take up too much room for us to carry it on the truck designed for it. We eventually won the argument and were allowed to use it without a cab so long as it was never driven by a human driver. Little did they know that its load space was underneath a second floor that came down to just a couple of inches over the top of the steering wheel, so when I loaded it I lay on my stomach on the seat (probably less stomach than I have now), worked the clutch and brake with my hands, keeping my head below the top steering wheel position and driving up the ramps on to the truck floor, under the second floor until the front wheels hit the front board and then stopping the engine and locking the brakes I wriggled backwards until it was possible to stand up.

When twenty tractors and the various associated manufacturers were added to this we had quite a good show, something we could all be proud of, especially those of us who had never previously been involved in this kind of show. There was also a lot of equipment to do with forestry work to demonstrate. It was possible that the sale of forestry equipment to work the vast tracts of woodland in Sweden was a more important market than the agricultural one. We had several kinds of saws, a wonderful machine for removing bark from tree trunks; there was a machine for chopping brash and small branches into wood chips to use for fuel in the many wood burning stoves on the market, one of which was demonstrated on our show site. We also had a dustbin trailer for use behind a tractor suitable for the small municipalities so abundant in Sweden. This unit we filled with wood chips from the chopper and tipped them, as part of our demonstration, by the wood-burning stove chap, who sat all day firing up his four stoves. When we found that the Major was short of power to drive this chopper, our solution was to disable the governor until the engine would turn over at some fantastic amount of revolutions, which it was never designed for, open the throttle flat out and ram wood into the chopper feed until the engine was held from revving so hard it might burst, then if the revs dropped to ease the wood supply, if they rose to a screaming crescendo just to ram more wood into the feed mouth. We never had any trouble from that tractor or its PTO shaft all through the tour and that tractor was the one carrying our fuel supply in a large trailer tank, several hundreds of gallons. When all the stakes were down it always arrived first at the destination and was always the last to leave; it did hours and hours of demonstration work and 2300 miles on the road. Never doubt the toughness of a Major.

The chips this exhibit produced, as I have said, were used by our friend the wood-burner man. He had his four stoves and a table with a chair, and would sit there all day offering his clients a drink, usually vodka. Where he obtained it goodness knows, as it was almost impossible to buy it in Sweden at that time; there were no pubs, no off-licences and the commercial shops were not allowed to sell booze at all. Each town usually had one govern-ment-owned booze shop which only opened two hours in an afternoon. We never asked him how he obtained it but it was excellent as the weather became colder to walk up to see if he needed any more chips for the stoves and be offered a nice warming drink. He had a simple recipe for a winter drink, which was to pour coffee into a cup

126

until the bottom was invisible then pour in vodka until it was visible then coffee then vodka and so on until the cup was full. We usually only had one each day, but the effects were surprising. I often wondered if he made the stuff from trees. We often spoke about it, asking if it was distilled from birch sap or maybe wood chips, but he would always reply 'Et es a special secret.'

As we worked further south during May I had a letter from Betty telling me she was probably pregnant again and how pleased our parents were. But I was worried about the situation in view of the previous problems when her pregnancy had met such a disastrous end. I did manage to speak with her and hoped I encouraged her a little; at least I could give her the news that we were not working at Whitsuntide so I felt it possible to do a quick visit home for the weekend. I had been saving hard and some of my allowance could be used to buy an air ticket from Copenhagen to London. One of my colleagues elected to go with me to visit a girl friend who lived in London. We arranged for Betty to travel to London Airport to meet me, and my friend Terry volunteered to drive the van down there. Whilst I was busy arranging this Henry had a letter from his wife giving the same happy news, but she was suffering quite badly in these early stages and hoped he could soon return home. Henry could not travel with us to London owing to his position as team leader involving him in some promotion work for Ford Sweden, but I had the impression he might not return to Sweden after the July holiday; this left me wondering who might replace him, in case it was someone who might perhaps not provide such a happy base for our team spirit. We all mixed so well and really enjoyed our life out there, although our relationship with the Swedish side of the team might just take a step down for a few days mostly due, I am sure, to language difficulties, since we were by no means antagonistic to one another.

Leaving the team in Malmö my colleague and I took the ferry to Copenhagen to catch our flight to London. As we left Denmark, Betty would have been already on the road in the Ford van. So she could rest on the way if she felt off colour they took a flask of coffee and put a mattress and pillow in the back of the van. (In view of the previous experience she was taking great care of herself in these early days.) Our flight to London was quite fabulous, the aircraft being a Caravelle and the first jet I had ever been in. Very few passengers were aboard, so we asked the stewardess if we could visit the flight deck. We were eventually invited to go forward to see the pilot, who showed us the many instruments and controls; but to me in my innocence it seemed unreal that the pilot could turn round and talk to us, telling us we were travelling at 550 mph and 30,000 feet up whilst no one was looking where we were going. Now I know it would serve no purpose to look ahead but to a motorist it seems very odd indeed that all this forward speed gave no one any care about what might be in front.

When I arrived at London airport the bad news broke: Betty and Terry had been involved in a road accident and both were in Derby Royal Infirmary, but not badly injured. The airline had arranged a flight to Birmingham for me so I could get home as soon as possible. You may imagine my feelings. After telephoning the hospital I was somewhat reassured and travelled on the plane in better spirits, finally arriving by train in the early morning. At the hospital I found Betty with a hole in her knee where the choke control had dug into it and some skin missing from the back of her neck, Terry not breathing too well because his ribs had collided rather heavily with the steering wheel, and both rather bruised and crestfallen by their misfortune. Apparently a miner coming off shift had run out of a side turning into the side of the van as it travelled along the main road. The van must have gone down the road on its radiator grille as this was gravel-rashed all up the front; buckled wheels; broken windscreen; broken dashboard; switches and wires hanging around loose all over the cab; the spare wheel, loosed from its holder at considerable speed, had climbed up Betty's back, taking skin from her neck and pushing her down into the dashboard before departing through the windscreen. This accident I am sure is where I get my hatred of seat belts from. Now before you all jump on me, let me say that I am quite sure the spare wheel would have taken Betty's head off if she had been fastened in the seat and unable to be pushed forward out of the way. I often wondered what the people thought who had to sort out the wreckage finding a man and woman, married but not to each other, involved in an accident and carrying a mattress and blanket in the back of the vehicle.

All's well that ends well. Returning home later in the day with instructions to rest we were able to look at the problem with better feelings. But it was a narrow escape. We collected the van and unbelievably it could still be driven, but it was written off and so went for scrap. I now had to think of my next move. I was due back in Sweden on the Monday but I figured to telephone the office at Dagenham and explain the situation. Without prompting from me they assumed I had flown home *after* hearing of the accident and told me to stay for the week before returning to duty. That is one reason I have always felt a great admiration for Ford: on this and other occasions they have treated my personal problems as their own.

After a few days the doctor decided there was little

threat to the baby and so we decided to visit the Isle of Man. Remember Betty lived in a remote cottage and now had no vehicle, the old Wolseley having been despatched to the car breaker some time before, so it seemed reasonable that she would spend some weeks with our friends over there and then live with my parents until I returned from Sweden for good. Those of you who have read my earlier ramblings will recall the previous visits to the Isle of Man for the TT races and . . . What do you think? Yes, it was now TT week again, so off we went. Betty was established in the Wembley Hotel and we departed on the Friday morning to Hillberry to watch the race.

My previous telephone calls to Dagenham had established that I would return to Sweden on the Sunday night ready for work on Monday morning, but a last-minute message from Dagenham told me that when I arrived in Copenhagen on my return journey I should take a train to Hamburg, stay at the Hotel Rex and wait for someone to contact me, 'and you can take a look at a demonstration site we are considering using later in the year, we should like your opinion on the soil conditions, etc.' What a break for me! I cheerfully put my travelling expenses down on my expense form and so the trip home cost me nothing.

The journey back really was a marathon. After the race we took a bus back to Douglas, goodbyes were said and I caught the boat back to Liverpool, taxi to the railway station, 10.30 pm train to Crewe, train to London, 9.30 am tube to the air terminal, bus to Heathrow, plane to Copenhagen, taxi to the station, train to Hamburg, taxi to the hotel 7.30 pm; collected next morning by Bill Baker, a supervisor in sales promotion department, and then around Hamburg, eventually arriving at a large field which was available to Ford in October for a large tractor demonstration. We walked the field, digging into it to see what the soil was like. I commented that it would not provide a very severe test of tractors and that the access was bad if thousands of people were expected to visit each day. Bill rejoined that we probably did not want too many visitors and light easy soil would be just what was wanted. I was to see much more of this field later.

During our trip around the city Bill told me he had been stationed in Hamburg during the war and knew it pretty well. He suggested we did a tour of the night life later in the evening. I could do no more than agree. We dined and walked down the Reeperbahn, the infamous street of nightlife, calling at a few bars and noticing the still devastated ruins left over from the war. It really must have been terrible to have been caught up in those air raids; even fifteen years later many areas were just rubble. We ended up in a rather small bar, just talking and enjoying a beer, when we heard an English accent – well, nearly English, it was very obvious the language came from Liverpool! A few lads were sitting at a nearby table with empty glasses, words bubbling away in this attractive accent. We eventually spoke to them and chatted for a few minutes, being told they were appearing at a local night club, but no they had no money and so could not have another beer. 'Rubbish,' Bill said and ordered a round of refills. They told us they were called The Beatles and they were broke. How times change!

On with my journey . . . back to Copenhagen by train, train to Helsingør boat to Helsinborg, train to Halmstad, taxi to the hotel and I had rejoined the demonstration team in Sweden. Looking back over the week it came home to me how my life had changed, how I had strayed from my village roots with my free-and-easy ways and

131

lifestyle, never again to be a free agent, my responsibilities began to cage me like a captive bird, but as yet not too severely.

Now back at work life went on as before: putting up site, taking down site, living in good hotels and getting low on money; yes, even £1500 does not last long in Sweden. The day arrived when something had to be done about it, telephone calls to Dagenham brought another £2000 and a cryptic message 'What are you doing with it? You have had more money than any man I know'. I just responded with the message 'When are you going to finally employ me?' and just carried on working towards our two weeks' holiday in July.

In preparation for our holiday we left our trucks in Örebro and took the demonstration van to Stockholm, leaving it at the Ford factory. A taxi took us to Bromma for our flight home, but we were obviously 'bumped'. The flight was full, but another would be available in two hours' time. Five hours later we were boarding not a Caravelle as I had anticipated we would, but an old Constellation. This aircraft gave me the impression BEA, as it was then, had really scraped the bottom of the barrel to find something that would fly, it had been used for long distance flying I am sure, and was the only aircraft I have ever flown in that had sleeping bunks folded into the roof. As we stood on the end of the Bromma runway the engines went through the flight check and then put on full power for take off. Bromma has a very short runway (they have a new airport now, but we are looking back some thirty years) and the Constellation shuddered until it seemed every rivet jangled as the power poured on, we accelerated and as this happened the overhead bunks started to fall into the sleeping position. It was quite terrifying but we arrived home safely and I am sure were all greeted affectionately. I know I was, by Betty now back from the Isle of Man, a bit larger and very sunburnt and obviously in good health.

After a few days at home we decided to visit Scotland and so hired a Consul car, we enjoyed the scenery and the friendly people and then decided to visit the Isle of Skye, by this time I was running out of money again – English this time – and decided to change a Swedish note at the bank in Kyle of Lochalsh. An elderly gentleman took my note and retreated to the rear of the one-room bank, where I could see him thumbing through various coloured folders before eventually returning. Waving the Swedish note he enquired, 'Has it been in the family varra long?' After some more conversation he telephoned his head office and gave me money. We were solvent again.

11

RETURNING home nearly at the end of our holiday I found a message asking me to telephone John Prentice, my supervisor at Dagenham. 'Call in the office before you return to Sweden' was the request. I did of course and was introduced to a new member of our team, John Bayliss. We were to travel back to Sweden together and I was to try and familiarise him with our work as we went. John Prentice could now tell me I was officially employed by Ford and must sign an agreement, furthermore to my intense surprise I was now the team leader because Henry was not returning to Sweden but working in England to be near his wife. I refrained from saying 'What about *my* wife?' and just went off to catch the plane. From mending balers to becoming a regular flyer on business had taken less than a year.

Now there were changes. John took over my number four truck and continued to be responsible for putting up and taking down our 40-foot tower, I inherited the 15 cwt Thames van with its PA system and accompanied Elof Ender the Swedish tour manager to many public-relations gatherings, radio interviews, press talks, etc. We developed a really good rapport. It was very enjoyable and indeed rubbed off onto our teams; we began to socialise more in the evenings and on the occasional outing when time allowed. We made a good team but never again could I relax after the day's work and enjoy a nice evening with my colleagues. I was now locked into a press briefing on the morning we arrived in town, when an invitation would be issued to the press and radio people to attend a dinner in the evening. Of course alcohol was not easy to obtain unless you were having a meal. Our hotel was usually the best in town, specially chosen, no doubt, because it had a good dining room where the Ford dinner could be held. The Swedish drink-drive laws at that time were extremely strict; any alcohol at all that could be traced in your blood meant a prison sentence, so all our guests arrived by taxi in anticipation of a real good booze up, and they were never disappointed.

Speeches in Swedish, interviews with the press and radio including some for me in English, then the time would arrive for a pre-dinner drink. This was not usually your cheap sherry or white wine; our guests had whisky poured into them from the word go – not just one, either. Eventually we would go to the table . . . white wine with the first course then maybe another short speech with a glass of schnapps, knocked back at one go, another course perhaps with red wine, another short speech and another glass of schnapps and so on until the meal was finished around midnight. In England we might expect that after the meal most people would go home, but the Swedish people are not your run-of-the-mill namby-pamby race. They would often keep drinking until five or six in the morning, when Elof and I would pour them into taxis and retire to bed ourselves, knowing we had to be back on site at 8.30 am.

The other exhausting thing about this life, apart from having a dinner perhaps three times a week, was that it was never very dark at night. So we might start dinner in the sunshine, with twilight around midnight; but ages before our guests had gone home the sun would be shining again and then we had to try and recover from our alcoholic stupor and sleep the two or three hours we

135

had left before breakfast. Do not let anyone tell you how easy life on the road is.

I now had a well-paid job which I enjoyed (apart from too many functions), a wife and hoped soon to have a family. I had nowhere else to go so had to enjoy Sweden. At least I could unwind driving my demonstration van, which I soon learned to broadside around corners in a controlled slide. Most of the roads we were running on now were made from loose gravel, graded each week to keep them fairly smooth, and this surface was ideal for playing rally driving on. Very soon none of the Swedish team would ride with me, but I enjoyed the loose-surface driving. As we went further north the nights got longer and colder. After being told by a Swedish farmer that only the English would go to the land of the midnight sun and erect floodlights, we had stopped using them, but now we again put them up and flooded our site with light each evening, much to the joy of the local teenagers who came to the site and had an impromptu disco in the open air.

We had seen the midnight sun but what about the land of free love I had been so teased about before I left England? Well there is a story I can tell but no names will be used as I do not wish to be the cause of any marriage problems.

One of my colleagues developed rather a close relationship with a student who originally came to the site to help the local tractor dealer give out leaflets and act as a kind of receptionist. The need to look attractive obviously went with the job and the Swedish girls are indeed very attractive to look at. Certainly this young lady attracted my friend; he started to take dinner with her, so our little dining club as we called it was often missing two people, he with his lady and me at a press function. As we moved on she came to a few demonstrations, perhaps

136

with a little financial help, until we arrived in her home town, at which stage our colleague was invited to stay at her home. She duly arrived in Daddy's car and carried him away. Of course we were all fascinated. It appears that he was made welcome, fed well and taken to a local dance, taken back home and into her bed. During the night an irate father was hammering on the door insisting they made less noise – he could not get to sleep. The next night he made them move to a back bedroom.

Whether such free behaviour is regarded as enlightened or as morally lax, it may well have its origins in earlier historic circumstances. Possibly in the past when travel was not so easy, staying overnight was the only way young people could meet and do their courting. In fact this was borne out by a deserted village near one of our demonstration sites. When we asked why no one lived there the answer was that the houses were owned by people who lived miles away in the forests; when horses were the only transport it was not possible to come to the church and back home in the short winter days, so an overnight stay was needed in a house near the church. I was told that on a certain saint's day, the name of which escapes me, the teenagers were allowed to use these houses, just the one day each year, and again this would be a method of young people who lived in these remote forests meeting one another and forming friendships, alliances and generally preparing for marriage. In modern times most of them drive in cars but the traditional way is still used by some, the girl arriving on horseback in her furs riding sidesaddle and the boy also riding to the assignation. I have little doubt that the parents would bring the daughter to within easy reach of the village with a car and horsebox, unload the horse and later take it home again in the horsebox; but in the old days how

137

romantic it must have been meeting one's beau, perhaps seen only two or three times, and now the great day had arrived when a shy girl, after exchanging many letters, would move in with him for the whole night, knowing with certainty if she became pregnant there would be a marriage and another family's children would be joined together to form a new branch and continue the line.

Our last dealer in Sweden was at a town called Luleå just below the Arctic Circle. It was now September and we were experiencing quite sharp frost, but the autumn leaves with their wonderful colours had to be seen to be believed. This dealer, who told us his area was as big as Switzerland, Belgium and Luxembourg all joined together, was I believe the most northerly main dealer in Sweden. He mentioned one Fordson Major he had sold to a farmer and the journey, made in winter, meant he had to leave the Major running on the truck or it became so cold it would not start. The tractor was always kept in the large animal shed all Swedish farms seem to have that houses everything in the winter, so it was certain to start in the morning and when outside it would never have the engine stopped. The dealer travelled round his customers once each year, using a large American car and taking all the sales reps to each settlement in turn where the farmers would come to discuss the year's requirements with them. Otherwise all transactions had to be by telephone.

We stayed in a hotel on the side of a lake with the town on the other side. We were told that the lake froze over in October and very soon no one bothered to drive round by the road, just simply drove across the lake. Apparently darkness came in November and for six weeks it was perpetual night until one day the sun's rim would be seen on the horizon for the first time. Then the first feast of the year would be held. It was not so dark

138

when we were there but the days were indeed very short compared to those we had experienced further south. At least I have a certificate to say I crossed the Arctic Circle, as did my colleagues, having travelled especially to obtain this one day.

Just to prove a point!

Now demonstrations were a little less frantic, as we were doing only one each week. Ever since Henry had left the team in July I had been demonstrating the radio-controlled Dexta and gradually becoming more proficient, but still feeling just driving it about was not a good way to demonstrate it; it showed no obvious advantage over a normal tractor, although it certainly drew the crowds and the press. Now I had time to think about it I realised I must have another tractor to drive behind it, showing how one man could drive two tractors. We rigged up a second tractor and off I went to plough: two tractors, four furrows, one man. It now seemed a better show but it is very difficult to explain how difficult it is to turn one tractor, lift the plough, keep that one going in the correct direction whilst lifting the second plough and steering this second tractor. Later using reversible ploughs it was even more complicated. However, I eventually mastered the system and could provide a good demonstration.

During our stay in Luleå the long-awaited message came giving us what we thought would be our instructions to return home. No: we were to drive our equipment to Hamburg. I understood now why I had been told to visit Hamburg in June. There was to be a dealer convention held there and we were to be part of the field team.

About the time we received this message I was walking down the ramp into the dealer's workshop when my ankle turned and down I went. This I had done before and partly cured it by sitting still and reciting all the many words I could remember that do not appear in the Oxford dictionary, anyway giving my ankle time to ease a little. It was then likely to swell very rapidly until I could not wear my shoe, at which stage I bound it up with sticking plaster (not the elastic type) and limped away wearing a canvas shoe. It usually recovered after a few days and life returned to normal until the next time. Now in Sweden they take the wellbeing of the population very much to heart so before I really knew what was happening a keen type in the workshop had sent for the ambulance and despite my protestations off we went to the hospital. I was laid on a flat bed, examined by a doctor and soon two very attractive nurses were gumming up my leg with sloppy white plaster. Most efficient! In one hour I was back in circulation with instructions to rest it for two weeks and then return. No one took any notice of my protestations that I had to drive to Hamburg in three days time. That is impossible, I was told. But they had put a piece of metal under my foot so it contacted the ground when walking and by sheer chance this was just the right height for the big toe they had left uncovered to contact the accelerator and produce some action from the van. There was a problem to this however – it was so cold down in the bottom of the van, even with the heater

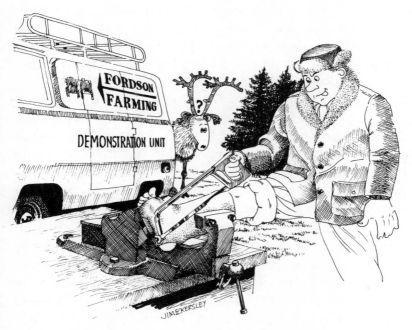

An unusual demonstration on a tractor site.

141

on full blast, that my toe disappeared from this world, at least it felt so. Two days later (the day before we were due to pack up for the last time in Sweden), I had had enough; the people visiting the site could see a mad Englishman with his leg in the service van vice sawing away at a plaster cast with a hacksaw blade. Eventually I managed to remove it, plastered the ankle with sticking plaster – and I was ready to drive to Hamburg.

Leaving our Swedish friends, after a great celebration going on for most of the night, we set off on our 1000-mile journey to Hamburg, down to Malmö, across to Copenhagen, and on into Germany, arriving at Hotel Rex on the Kielerstrasse three days later. The next day we were contacted by Bill Baker, John Prentice, and a man I had not met before, Paul Coles, he of the wonderful voice, our commentator for the dealer convention demonstration to be held in the field I had seen on my previous visit. Our trucks were delivered to the site and left in charge of a German watchman, while we were given a briefing as to our duties in Hamburg – the presentation of a new tractor to every Fordson dealer in Europe. We were to prepare and operate a thirty-minute demonstration featuring these new tractors and also to present as many as possible of the machines made by other manufacturers but using Fordson tractors as the base product, e.g. County, Roadless, Doe, etc. The list just went on and on.

The next day equipment started to arrive, loaders, diggers, a Howard Trencher . . . We spent nearly one week unloading, then setting up, and afterwards our new tractors arrived. We found we had three only and sixteen implements to demonstrate; in half an hour we had to change implements eight times and one change meant changing implement and a tractor rear wheel. The

142

planning that went into this thirty-minute presentation was really almost unbelievable. Our new tractors were the first Super Majors any of us had seen, indeed we had never heard of the Super Major before we arrived in Hamburg. Their new features were the introduction of inboard disc brakes, diff lock and draught control hydraulics for the first time on a Major. The reason we only had three was that only these three had been produced as almost hand-built prototypes, while the factory was still making Power Majors. I will not bore you with too many details but sufficient to say we had three grandstands built around our demo ring, with the English commentary from Paul being translated into five languages. Each dealer had a small handset which he tuned to his language.

Our carefully planned show was started by myself driving into the ring the first Super Major. We had the Hamburg fire service to blast it with high pressure water around the footplates, whilst I stood on the seat (no time to dismount), collecting my share of the water. The programme was then to drive at full speed into a brick wall (built of tea chests, I add), and stop just before hitting it whilst the commentator went on about our new waterproof brakes. As I exited another unit would enter the ring whilst the one I had been using was reworked for another entry. In this case a plough was fitted and the rear wheel changed for one without any tread so we could demonstrate how our diff lock worked. Just try fitting a plough and changing a rear wheel in three minutes under pressure, as a few hundred dealers were on site! The idea was to plough a little way, release the diff lock so the plain tyre would spin and then engage the diff lock again so its advantage could plainly be seen by the audience. But I found the Major just ploughed on even without a diff lock, so here I was trying to apply one rear wheel brake to induce wheel spin on the other wheel so I could show how the diff lock would stop this problem.

Many things like this happened but our demonstration went off very well. It was repeated three times for different dealers and at last the loading-up stage was reached. Part of the deal with the landowner was we would plough the field before we left. As I have already said, it was a large field crossed by a telephone line, a pole in each hedge and one in the middle. Well, one of my team of 'skilled' demonstrators managed to run into the only pole in a twenty-acre field and knock it down.

* * *

We left Hamburg with some regrets – we had become used to the night life – but going home was something else, looked forward to by all. Two days later we left our trucks at Boreham and off we went for a few days' break. I had arranged to collect a new 5 cwt van from the factory to replace the one lost in the crash, so I arrived home in the late afternoon to see Betty for the first time since July. She was by now quite a portly girl but still very happy and looking in extremely good health. Her worries had gone and the baby was due in about two months.

After our break it was time to paint and repair our equipment. This was to take us up to the end of January. In the meantime I had lodgings in a pub in Boreham village, as the Ford base could not cope with this influx of demonstrators. I went home each Friday afternoon and returned on Monday morning. One day a message came to say Betty had given birth to a son, so off I went home as quickly as possible to see a happy and contented Betty and a new son, William Nicholas, had arrived. Of course our families were as happy as we were. It was a time of

144

satisfaction after all my wanderings and Betty's adventures living on her own.

Our new contentment was short-lived. I was told to prepare the equipment for another Tracteuropa caravan to France starting in late February. It seemed such a short time to spend with my new and expanded family. Another trip was planned after France, this time to Germany in the autumn and other journeys were to come along, domestic demonstrations, agricultural shows, a long caravan tour to Spain. There was to be little peace in the future, but maybe those adventures can be told in another book. I still call myself a tractor driver and operate from the tractor seat though as time goes on the seat becomes softer but the responsibility greater.

Do you wonder about Mr Woggins? Quite an old gentleman now, he lives in retirement, his beloved David Brown sold; but on nice afternoons he can be seen proudly escorting the pram down the lane near our cottage.

Farming Press Books & Videos

Below is a sample of the wide range of agricultural and veterinary books and videos we publish. For more information or for a free illustrated catalogue of all our publications please contact:

Farming Press Books & Videos
Miller Freeman Professional Ltd
Wharfedale Road, Ipswich IP1 4LG, United Kingdom
Telephone (01473) 241122   Fax (01473) 240501

Books

Tractors at Work: A Pictorial Review 1904–1994   Stuart Gibbard
A highly illustrated book showing the working history of tractors in Britain and emphasising the uses to which tractors were put.

Tractors since 1889   Michael Williams
An overview of the main developments in farm tractors from their stationary steam engine origins to the potential for satellite navigation. Colour and black-and-white illustrations.

World Harvesters   Bill Huxley
Photographs of a wide range of mechanical harvesters from all over the world from the earliest days up to the present are accompanied by informative captions and comment.

Farm Machinery   Brian Bell
Gives a sound introduction to a wide range of tractors and farm equipment, incorporating over 150 photographs.

Videos

The Massey-Ferguson Story   Michael Williams
From the early days of Wallis and the General Purpose tractor right through to modern high-spec models.

Fordson: the story of a tractor
Featuring the five main Fordson models from 1917 to the 1950s, this combines archive material with new film.

John Deere Two-cylinder Tractors, Vols One & Two
Michael Williams
Volume One gives a vivid portrayal of the early days from the Froelich replica to the Model G. Volume Two continues with the later development of two-cylinder tractors from the new styling to the 1960s.

Classic Farm Machinery: 1940–1970
Brian Bell, narrated by Chris Opperman
An outstanding selection of archive film extracts accompanied by a thoughtful commentary.

Farming Press Books & Videos is a division of Miller Freeman Professional Ltd which provides a wide range of media services in agriculture and allied businesses. Among the magazines published by the group are Arable Farming, Dairy Farmer, Farming News, Pig Farming *and* What's New in Farming. *For a specimen copy of any of these please contact the address above.*